The First World Congress of Nonlinear Analysts will be held under the auspices of the International Federation of Nonlinear Analysts and with the sponsorship of Embry-Riddle Aeronautical University, Florida Institute of Technology, Oak Ridge National Laboratory, Tampa Mayor's Office, UNESCO, University of Texas at San Antonio, U.S. Army Research Office, and Walter DeGruyter Publishers.

The Congress will be held at the Tampa Convention Center, 333 South Franklin, Tampa, Florida 33602 USA.

SPECIAL EVENTS

1. There will be a complimentary "Happy Hour" Reception Party on August 19th from 17:30–19:30 at the Hyatt Regency Hotel.

2. The Banquet will be held on Friday, August 21st at the Hyatt Regency Hotel. Happy Hour will be from 18:00 to 19:30 and dinner with wine from 19:30 to 22:00. The key note speaker at the banquet will be:
   Dr. Earle L. Messere, Technical Director, U.S. Navy, Washington, D.C.

3. Registration desks will be open on August 18th at the Tampa Convention Center from 16:00 to 20:00 hours. On August 19th, registration will be open from 8:00–17:00.

4. Remember that the deadline for the submission of manuscripts for the proceedings of the Congress is November 30, 1992. Early submission will be appreciated.

Titles of Organized Sessions

Qualitative Theory of Difference Equations (August 19–21, Room 6)

Periodic Solutions of Boundary Value Problems (August 21–22, Room 7)

Nonlinear Parabolic Problems (August 21–22, Room 1)

Differential Delay Equations & Applications in Biology and Medicine (August 25, Room 13)

Critical Point Theory & Hamiltonian Systems (August 21, Room 14)

Special Session Lyapunov's 100th Anniversary (August 19–24, Room C)

Math Epidemiology (August 21–22, Room 15)

Nonconvex Analysis (August 25, Room 16)

Blow-up, Dead Cores & Quenching (August 19–20, Room 7)

Multiple Solutions of Nonlinear Differential Equations (August 25–26, Room 3)

Control Theory in Economics (August 19–20, Room 8)

Special Session on Poincare's Centenary (August 24, Room 13)

Nonlinear Waves (August 19–20, Room 13)

Neural Networks in Biomedicine (August 26, Room 2)

Fixed Point Theory & Related Topics (August 19–20, Room 3)

Global Bifurcations & Chaos (August 24, Room 9)

Nonlinear Oscillations (August 19–20, Room 10)

Structural Models in Ecology Theory & Applications (August 20, Room 14)

Models in Ecology: Spatial Heterogenity (August 19, Room 14)

Math Modeling of Enzyme Systems (August 20–21, Room 18)

Computational Methods for Parameter Estimation and Control (August 22–24, Room 3)

Nonlinear Controlled Systems (August 24, Room 4)

Nonlinear Problems in Superconductivity (August 22, Room 6)

Accretive & Monotone Operator Theory (August 25–26, Room 10)

Evolution Equations (August 24–25, Room 8)

Nonlinear Aspects of the Analysis & Computations for Microelectronic Devices (In memory of F. Odeh) (August 21, Room 11)

Hereditary Systems and Their Applications (August 25–26, Room 7)

Positive Discrete Dynamical Systems (August 19–20, Room 1)

Geometric Methods (August 19–20, Room 12)

Nonlinear Operators (August 19–21, Room 4)

Optimization & Optimal Control (August 25–26, Room 18)

Bifurcation (August 25–26, Room 6)

Duality & Variational Methods (August 26, Room C)

Chaos (August 21, Room 12)

Fixed Point Theory (August 24, Room 11)

Parabolic Equations (August 20–21, Room 17)

Stochastic Systems (August 25–26, Room 17)

Environmental Problems (August 22, Room 2)

General (August 25–26, Room C)

Computational Methods (August 22–24, Room 3)

Bifurcation, Chaos & Artificial Intelligence in Nonlinear Electonics
(August 19, Room B)

Stability Problems in Nonlinear Compartmental Systems with Pipes and Delays
(August 25–26, Room 11)

Nonlinear Stochastic Systems (August 24–25, Room 15)

Recent Development of Reliability Analysis & Modeling (August 19–20, Room 15)

Asymptotic Behavior of Nonlinear Systems Attractors and Confinors: Application to
Biology. (August 19, Room 9)

Math Modeling of Oscillator Interactions Dynamics with Special Emphasis on Immune
Systems Mechanisms. (August 25, Room 9)

Neural Networks: Algorithms and Applications (August 25–26, Room 4)

PROGRAM OF EXPOSITORY LECTURES

Wednesday, August 19

=============================== 10:00-12:00   Ballrooms B & C ===============================

10:00 **Opening ceremonies**
   Introductory Remarks: V. Lakshmikantham and Chris P. Tsokos.

11:00 Chaos and artificial intelligence (A Laser/Audio/Video presentation).
   (1) **Leon Chua,** University of California, Berkeley.

12:00-14:00 ....Lunch

Session I
8:30–12:00   Ballroom B

8:30 Mathematical modeling of biodegradation of organisms in ground water.
   (2) **Mary F. Wheeler**, Rice University, Houston.

9:30-10:00 .... Break

10:00 Theory of multipolar fluids.
   (3) **J. Necas**, Mathematical Institute of the Czechoslovakian Academy of Sciences, Czechoslovakia.

11:00 Concentrations in fluid flow and related equations.
   (4) **A. Majda**, Princeton University, Princeton.

12:00-14:00 .... Lunch

Session II
8:30–12:00   Ballroom C

8:30 Nonlinear PDE problems arising in U.S. industry.
   (5) **A. Friedman**, University of Minnesota, Minneapolis.

9:30-10:00 .... Break

10:00 Set-valued analysis and viability theory.
   (6) **J.P. Aubin**, Univ. de Paris-Dauphine, France.

11:00 Prevalence: A translation-invariant "almost every" on infinite dimensional spaces.
   (7) **Jim Yorke**, University of Maryland, College Park.

12:00-14:00 .... Lunch

Session IIII
8:30–12:00   Room 11

8:30 Some thoughts on parabolic problems.
   (8) **Ray Redheffer**, UCLA, Los Angeles.

9:30-10:00 .... Break

10:00 On some nonlinear problems in stochastic calculus.
   (9) **A.N. Shiryaev**, Steklov Mathematical Institute, Russia.

11:00 Stochastic systems and nonlinear analysis.
   (10) **V. Skorokhod**, Ukrainian Academy of Science, Ukraine.

12:00-14:00 .... Lunch

Session I
8:30–12:00   Ballroom B

8:30 Stochastic theories of chaos in high dimensional systems.
(11) **James Glimm,** SUNY at Stony Brook, Stony Brook.

9:30-10:00 .... **Break**

10:00 A survey on nonlinear elliptic systems arising in the context of ergodic control and game theory.
(12) **A. Bensoussan*,** INRIA, France, and **J. Frehse,** Bonn University, Germany.

11:00 Nonlinear problems in stochastic processes.
(13) **G. Kallianpur,** University of North Carolina, Chapel Hill.

12:00-14:00 .... **Lunch**

Session II
8:30–12:00   Ballroom C

8:30 Solving nonlinear systems of equations.
(14) **S. Smale,** University of California, Berkeley.

9:30-10:00 .... **Break**

10:00 On the modal control for nonlinear Lure systems.
(15) **A.A. Voronov,** VINITI, Russia.

11:00 Differential-geometric, computational methods for multiparameter nonlinear problems.
(16) **W. Rheinboldt,** University of Pittsburgh, Pittsburgh.

12:00-14:00 .... **Lunch**

Session III
8:30–12:00   Room 11

8:30 Aspects of singular perturbation theory in physiology.
(17) **Jane Cronin Scanlon,** Rutgers University, New Jersey.

9:30-10:00 .... **Break**

10:00 TBA.
(18) **V.S. Vladimirov,** Russia.

11:00 Decomposition and Feedback control in nonlinear dynamic systems.
(19) **F.L. Chernousko,** Institute for Problems in Mechanics, RAS, Russia.

12:00-14:00 .... **Lunch**

Session I
8:30–12:00   Ballroom B

8:30 New spectral representations of mixing dynamical systems.
(20) **I. Prigogine** and **I. Antoniou**, Univ. Libre de Bruxelles, Belgium.

9:30-10:00 .... Break

10:00 International Federation of Nonlinear Analysts (**IFNA**) Meeting, Ballroom B.

10:30 Round Table Conference I, Ballroom B.
Chaired by: **Jagdish Chandra** and **P. Davis.**
Panelists: **David Dence,** Underwater Sound Lab, New London.
David S. Ross, Eastman Kodak Co., Rochester, New York.
John Bownds, Oak Ridge National Laboratory, Oak Ridge.
Dale Thoe, Allison Gass Turbine Division of General Motors, Indianapolis.

12:00-14:00 .... Lunch

Session II
8:30–12:00   Ballroom C

8:30 On special gradient maximum principles for nonlinear elliptic equations.
(21) **Larry Payne,** Cornell University, Ithaca.

9:30-10:00 .... Break

10:30 Round Table Conference II, Ballroom C.
Chaired by: **Chris P. Tsokos.**
Panelists: **Richard A. Johnson,** University of Wisconsin, Madison.
Way Kuo, Iowa State University, Ames.
Abdel Hamead, Kuwait University, Kuwait.
Vladimir P. Savchuk, Dniepropetrovsk State University, Russia.

12:00-14:00 .... Lunch

Session III
8:30–12:00   Room 11

8:30 Norbert Weiner's brain waves.
(22) **Steven Strogatz** Massachusetts Institute of Technology, Cambridge.

Session I
8:30–12:00   Ballroom B

8:30 Traveling waves in a cylinder.
(23) **L. Nirenberg,** New York University, New York.

9:30-10:00 .... Break

10:00 Quasivariational differential systems.
(24) **James Serrin,** University of Minnesota, Minneapolis.
11:00 TBA.
(25) **Ju. S. Osipov,** Russian Academy of Science, Russia.

12:00-14:00 .... Lunch

Session II
8:30–12:00   Ballroom C

8:30 Stabilization of unstable procedures: Computing unstable steady states via time marching.
(26) **H. Keller,** California Institute of Technology, Pasadena.

9:30-10:00 .... Break

10:00 TBA
(27) **R. Sagdeev,** University of Maryland, College Park.
11:00 Some nonlinear dynamic features of adaptive control systems.
(28) **Y.G. Kevrekidis,** Princeton University, Princeton.

12:00-14:00 .... Lunch

Session I
8:30–12:00   Ballroom B

8:30 Degree theory: Old and new.
(29) **F. Browder**, Rutgers University, New Brunswick.

9:30-10:00 .... Break

10:00 The variational methods for dynamical systems.
(30) **P. Rabinowitz**, University of Wisconsin, Madison.

11:00 Ginzburg-Landau vortices.
(31) **H. Brezis**, Univ. Pierre et Marie Curie (Paris VI) and Rutgers University, New Brunswick.

12:00-14:00 .... Lunch

Session II
8:30–12:00   Ballroom C

8:30 Statistical methods to detect nonlinearity and chaos in time series data.
(32) **W.A. Brock**, University of Wisconsin, Madison.

9:30-10:00 .... Break

10:00 Recent developments in the theory of Navier-Stokes equations.
(33) **K. Masuda**, Rikkyo University, Japan.

11:00 Global stability: Injectivity and the Jacobian conjectures.
(34) **C. Olech**, Polish Academy of Science, Poland.

12:00-14:00 .... Lunch

Session I
8:30–12:00   Ballroom B

8:30 Subgradients and variational analysis.
(35) **R.T. Rockafellar,** University of Washington, Seattle.

9:30-10:00 .... **Break**

10:00 Stability of systems with incomplete corrections.
(36) **N.A. Kuznetsov,** Inst. of Information Problems, RAS, Russia.

11:00 Applications of generalized functions to propagating and deforming interfaces.
(37) **R. Kanwal,** Pennsylvania State University, University Park.

12:00-14:00 .... **Lunch**

Session II
8:30–12:00   Ballroom C

8:30 Investigation of the viscoelastic model when viscous coefficient tends to zero.
(38) **P.E. Sobolevskii,** The Hebrew University, Israel.

9:30-10:00 .... **Break**

10:00 New classes of operator equations: Results, applications, and open problems.
(39) **M. Krasnosel'skii,** Inst. of Information Problems, RAS, Russia.

11:00 Control problems and nonlinear analysis.
(40) **S.V. Emelyanov,** International Institute of Control Systems, Russia.

12:00-14:00 .... **Lunch**

Positive Discrete Dynamical Systems
14:00–17:15   Room 1
Chaired by: U. Krause and R. Nussbaum

14:00 Positive nonlinear operators associated with isoperimetric eigenvalue problems in algebras.
(41) **Peter J. Bushell**, University of Sussex, England.

14:45 Order three may imply order.
(42) **Takao Fujimoto**, Okayama University, Japan.

15:30-15:45 .... Break

15:45 Positive discrete dynamical systems.
(43) **Ulrich Krause**, Universitat Bremen, Germany.

16:30 Cardinality estimates for omega limit sets of some nonlinear operators.
(44) **Roger D. Nussbaum**, Rutgers University, New Brunswick.

Fixed Point Theory and Related Topics
14:00–16:30   Room 3
Chaired by: E. Fadell and A. Kirk

14:00 Borsuk-Ulam theorems and variational problems with symmetries.
(45) **Thomas Bartsch**, Universitat Heidelberg, Germany.

14:45 External Schauder approximations and applications.
(46) **Jean-Bernard Baillon**, Universite Lyon, France.

15:30-15:45 .... Break

15:45 Approximating fixed points of nonexpansive mappings.
(47) **Ronald E. Bruck**, University of Southern California, Los Angeles.

Nonlinear Dynamic Models in Economic Theory
14:00–17:15   Room 5
Chaired by: M. Majumdar

14:00 Limit integration theorems for monotone functions and parametric continuity in economic models.
(48) **M. Majumdar***, Cornell University, Ithaca and **P. Dutta**, Columbia University, New York.

14:45 Chaotic models in economic theory and econometrics.
(49) **M. El-Gamal**, California Institute of Technology, Pasadena.

15:30-15:45 .... Break

15:45 Dynamic economic models with irreversibility and uncertainty.
(50) **L. Olson**, University of California, Riverside.

16:30 Survival under uncertainty.
(51) **S. Roy**, Erasmus University, The Netherlands.

Qualitative Theory of Difference Equations
14:00–17:15   Room 6
Chaired by: R.P. Agarwal

14:00 Recent results in difference equations and difference inequalities.
  (52) **R.P. Agarwal**, University of Singapore, Singapore.

14:45 Equivalence of discrete Euler equations and discrete Hamiltonian systems.
  (53) **C. Ahlbrandt**, University of Missouri, Columbia.

15:30–15:45 .... **Break**

15:45 Invariant foliation for nonautonomous systems.
  (54) **B. Aulbach**, Universitat Augsburg, Germany.

16:30 Oscillation theorems for a nonlinear difference equation.
  (55) **S.S. Cheng**, Southern Illinois University, Carbondale.

Blow-up, Dead Cores and Quenching
14:00–17:15   Room 7
Chaired by: C.Y. Chan and M.K. Kwong

14:00 Blow-up, dead cores and quenching.
  (56) **A. Friedman**, University of Minnesota, Minneapolis.

14:45 New results in quenching.
  (57) **C.Y. Chan**, University of Southwestern Louisiana, Lafayette.

15:30–15:45 .... **Break**

15:45 Blow-up versus global solvability for a class of nonlinear parabolic equations.
  (58) **H.M. Yin**, University of Notre Dame, Notre Dame.

16:30 Upper bounds for the life span of solutions to nonlinear systems of nonlinear wave equations.
  (59) **M. Rammaha**, University of Nebraska, Lincoln.

Control Theory in Economics
14:00–16:30   Room 8
Chaired by: E.N. Chukwu

14:00 Mathematical controlability theory of growth of wealth nations.
  (60) **E.N. Chukwu**, North Carolina State University, Raleigh.

14:45 Towards a global analysis of control systems.
  (61) **F. Colonius**, Universitat Augsburg, Germany.

15:30–15:45 .... **Break**

15:45 The emergence of inequality in a growing economy.
  (62) **Steven Durlauf**, Stanford University, Stanford.

Asymptotic Behavior of Nonlinear Systems: Attractors and Confinors: Application to Biology
14:00–16:30   Room 9
Chaired by: J. Demongeot

14:00 Asymptotic properties of nonlinear systems and applications in neuromodeling and medical imaging.
(63) **Jacques Demongeot**, TIMB Laboratoire d'informatique Medicale, France.

14:45 Modeling of the cell cycle: Proliferation and synchronization.
(64) **L. Demetrios**, Harvard University, Cambridge.

15:30-15:45 .... Break

15:45 Identification and quantification of attractor metamorphosis in digitized histopathologic images.
(65) **U.J. Balis**, University of Utah, Salt Lake City.

Engineering Applications
14:00–17:15   Room 11
Chaired by: C. Wimberly and R. Gibson

14:00 Nonlinear problems in Aerospace.
(66) **Stephen Sliwa**, Embry-Riddle Aeronautical University, Daytona Beach.

14:45 The extension of least median of squares regression of image processing.
(67) **H. Longbotham**, University of Texas, San Antonio.

15:30-15:45 .... Break

15:45 Nonlinear wave phenomena in petroleum applications.
(68) **R.E. Ewing**, University of Wyoming, Laramie.

16:30 Nonlinear interaction dynamics of multiple mobile automata.
(69) **P.K.C. Wang**, University of California, Los Angeles.

Elliptic Systems
14:00–17:15   Room 2
Chaired by: J. Hernandez

14:00 Maximum principles for elliptic systems and applications.
(70) **J. Hernandez**, Universidad Autonoma, Spain.

14:45 Nonhomogeneous degenerate eigenvalue problem.
(71) **P. Drabek**, Zapadoceska Univerzita Katedra, Czechoslovakia.

15:30-15:45 .... Break

15:45 Uniqueness and stability results of nonnegative solutions for semipositone problems in a ball.
(72) **R. Shivaji**, Mississippi State University, Mississippi State.

16:30 Solution of the inverse nodal problem on a rectangle.
(73) **J.R. McLaughlin**, Rensselaer Polytech Institute, Troy.

Nonlinear Operators
14:00–17:15   Room 4
Chaired by: J. Ize

14:00 On interpolation of nonlinear operators.
(74) **M. Bohm**, Humboldt Universitat - Berlin, Germany.

14:45 Equivalent degree theory for abelian groups.
(75) **J. Ize**, IIMAS-UNAM, Mexico.

15:30-15:45 ....**Break**

15:45 Some nonlinear results in abstract differential equations.
(76) **S. Zaidman**, University of Montreal, Canada.

16:30 Some applications and extensions of P-coercive variational inequalities.
(77) **D.D. Ang**, Ho Chi Minh City University, South Vietnam.

Nonlinear Oscillations
14:00–17:15   Room 10
Chaired by: J.R. Graef

14:00 Behavior of nonoscillatory solutions of forced second order neutral delay equations.
(78) **P.W. Spikes**, Mississippi State University, Mississippi State.

14:45 Regularity and asymptotics of solutions of some nonlinear ordinary differential equations.
(79) **V. Maric*** and **Z. Radasin**, University of Novi Sad, Yugoslavia.

15:30-15:45 ....**Break**

15:45 Oscillation of neutral differential equations.
(80) **S.W. Schultz**, Providence College, Providence.

16:30 On solutions of a neutral equation with an oscillatory coefficient.
(81) **J.R. Graef*** and **P.W. Spikes**, Mississippi State University, Mississippi State.

Geometric Methods
14:00–16:30   Room 12
Chaired by: C. Vargas

14:00 Frequency of entrainment in singularly perturbed systems.
(82) **J. Cronin-Scanlon**, Rutgers University, New Brunswick.

14:45 Phase transitions and phase field theory.
(83) **P.E. Souganidis**, Brown University, Providence.

15:30-15:45 ....**Break**

15:45 Searching for periodic orbits in a four dimensional symplectic map (using a homotopic method).
(84) **C. Vargas**, Centro de Inves., Mexico.

Nonlinear Waves
14:00–17:15   Room 13
Chaired by: L. Debnath

14:00 Quantum gravity and integrable nonlinear waves.
(85) **Yuji Kodama**, Ohio State University, Columbus.

14:45 Solitary waves with spin.
(86) **Henry Warchall**, University of North Texas, Denton.

15:30-15:45 ....**Break**

15:45 New soliton equation for dipole chains.
(87) **E.S. Infeld**, University of College London, England.

16:30 Nonlinear instabilities of steady and oscillatory wave convection in a rotating system.
(88) **D.N. Riahi**, University of Illinois, Urbana.

Models in Ecology: Spatial Heterogenity
14:00–17:15   Room 14
Chaired by: T. Hallam and J. Cushing

14:00 Stability of Ecological models with delays.
(89) **T. Gard**, University of Georgia, Athens.

14:45 Optimal control of parabolic PDE governing beaver populations.
(90) **S. Lenhart**, University of Tennessee, Knoxville.

15:30-15:45 ....**Break**

15:45 Modeling stratified diffusion in biological invasions.
(91) **N. Shigasada**, Kyoto University, Japan.

16:30 Should a park be an island?
(92) **S. Cantrell**, University of Miami, Coral Gables.

Recent Developments of Reliability Analysis and Modeling
14:00–17:15   Room 15
Chaired by: A.N.V. Rao and C.P. Tsokos

14:00 Bayesian statistical approach to design of reliability models.
(93) **Vladimir P. Savchuk**, Dniepropetrovsk State University, Ukraine.

14:45 Applications of consecutive k-out-of-n reliability in selecting acceptance sampling strategies.
(94) **Haeil Ahn and Way Kuo**, Iowa State University, Ames.

15:30-15:45 ....**Break**

15:45 Some robustness issues in the Bayesian analysis of a Weibull failure model.
(95) **Alex S. Papadopoulos and Robert M. Hoekstra**, University of North Carolina, Charlotte.

16:30 A nonhomogeneous Poisson process for software reliability.
(96) **A.N.V. Rao*** and **Nalina Suresh**, University of South Florida, Tampa.

Boundary Value Problems
14:00–17:15   Room 16
Chaired by: Reza Aftabizadeh

14:00 Singular boundary value problems on the semi-infinite interval.
(97) **D. O'Regan**, University College of Galway, Ireland.

14:45 Boundary eigenvalue problems for magneto hydrodynamics.
(98) **R. Mennicken**, Universitat Regensberg, Germany.

15:30-15:45 .... Break

15:45 Existence of solutions for a strongly nonlinear second order ODE.
(99) **M.G. Huidobro**, and **R.Manasevich***, Universidad de Chile, Chile, and **F. Zanolin**, Universita di Udine, Italy.

16:30 Existence and nonexistence of solutions to some nonlinear two point boundary value problems at resonance.
(100) **Seppo Seikkila**, University of Oulu, Finland.

General I
14:00–17:15   Room 17
Chaired by: Gary W. Howell

14:00 Selection theorems for L^p-valued maps and their applications to implicit differential equations which are not solvable for the highest derivative.
(101) **T. Kaczynski**, Universite de Sherbrooke, Canada.

14:45 On the existence of weak extremal solutions for quasilinear elliptic and parabolic boundary value problems.
(102) **S. Carl**, Technische Hochschule Merseburg, Germany.

15:30-15:45 .... Break

15:45 Numeric solution of a stiff matrix Ricatti differential equation.
(103) **Gary W. Howell**, Florida Institute of Technology, Melbourne.

16:30 Nonlinear wave-wave interactions.
(104) **Don T. Resio*** and **Gary W. Howell**, Florida Institute of Technology, Melbourne.

General II
14:00–17:15   Room 18
Chaired by: A.S. Vatsala

14:00 Higher order slyding mode.
(105) **S.K. Korovin**, VNIISI, Russia.

14:45 Group theoretical methods for finite difference modeling.
(106) **V.A. Dorodnitsyn**, Keldish Institute of Applied Math, Russia.

15:30-15:45 .... Break

15:45 Recent trends and problems in the theory of nonlinear functional differential equations.
(107) **N.A. Azbelev**, Perm Russia.

16:30 TBA.
(108) **V.F. Krotov**, IPU, Russia.

Bifurcation, Chaos and Artificial Intelligence in Nonlinear Electronics
14:00–17:15   Room B
Chaired by: L. Chua and R. Marshall

14:00 The twist-and-flip paradigm in nonlinear electronic circuits.
(109) **R. Brown and L. Chua***, University of California, Berkeley.

14:45 Bifurcation and chaos from Chua's circuit: A state-of-the-art review.
(110) **M. Ogorzalek**, University of Mining and Metallurgy, Poland.

15:30-15:45 ....Break

15:45 Chaotic dynamics in cellular neural networks.
(111) **J. Nossek**, Technische Universitat Munchen, Germany.

16:30 Nonlinear image processing and motion detection via cellular neural networks.
(112) **T. Roska**, Hungarian Academy of Sciences, Hungary.

Lyapunov Centenary Session
14:00–17:15   Room C
Chaired by: S. Leela

13:45 Development of Lyapunov ideas for the hundred years: 1892-1992.
(113) **V.M. Matrosov**, Russian Academy of Science, Russia.

14:45 Boundedness and stability in functional differential equations.
(114) **T.A. Burton**, Southern Illinois University at Carbondale, Carbondale.

15:30-15:45 ....Break

15:45 A Lyapunov-Razumikhin method for functional differential equations.
(115) **Tetsuo Furumochi**, Shimane University, Japan.

16:30 A brief survey of Lyapunov's direct method and invariance principles.
(116) **John Haddock**, Memphis State University, Memphis.

Positive Discrete Dynamical Systems (cont.)
14:00–17:30   Room 1
Chaired by: U. Krause and R. Nussbaum

14:00 On positive nonlinear operators.
(117) **Anthony J.B. Potter**, University of Aberdeen, Scotland.

14:45 Random products of contractions.
(118) **Simeon Reich**, University of Southern California, Los Angeles.

15:30-16:00 .... Break

16:00 Positive operators in population dynamics.
(119) **Hal L. Smith**, Arizona State University, Tempe.

16:45 Strongly monotone discrete dynamical systems and applications to parabolic equations.
(120) **Peter Takac**, Vanderbilt University, Nashville.

Inertial Manifolds
14:00–17:30   Room 5
Chaired by: Roger Temam

14:00 Recent development in the theory of inertial manifolds.
(121) **R. Temam**, Indiana University, Bloomington and Universite de Paris-Sud, France.

14:45 Bifurcation computations on an approximate inertial manifold for the 2-D Navier-Stokes equations.
(122) **Michael Jolly**, Indiana University, Bloomington.

15:30-16:00 .... Break

16:00 Inertial manifolds for Navier-Stokes equations.
(123) **Minkyu Kwak**, Chonnam National University, Korea.

16:45 Instabilities and structure of the attractor for the Kolmogorov-Navier-Stokes equations.
(124) **Basil Nicolaenko**, Arizona State University, Tempe.

Nonsmooth Analysis and Optimization
14:00–17:30   Room 9
Chaired by: B.S. Mordukhovich

14:00 First and second order differentiability of convex functions on various Banach spaces.
(125) **J.M. Borwein**, University of Waterloo, Canada.

14:45 Implicit functions defined by generalized equations.
(126) **A.L. Dontchev**, Mathematical Reviews, Ann Arbor.

15:30-16:00 .... Break

16:00 Nonsmooth subdifferentials: Calculus and Applications.
(127) **A. Ioffe**, Technion, Israel.

16:45 Approximation of a set-valued mapping.
(128) **C. Lemarechal**, INRIA, France.

Fixed Points and Related Topics (cont.)
14:00–17:30   Room 3
Chaired by: E. Fadell and A. Kirk

14:00 Orientability and degree for nonlinear Fredholm mappings.
(129) **Patrick M. Fitzpatrick**, University of Maryland, College Park.

14:45 Applications of fixed point index theory to second order differential equations on manifolds.
(130) **Massimo Furi**, Universita di Firenza, Italy.

15:30-16:00 ....Break

16:00 Some applications of equivariant degree theory.
(131) **Kazimierz Geba**, University of Gdansk, Poland.

16:45 On some general principles in nonlinear analysis.
(132) **Andrzej Granas**, University of Montreal, Canada.

Semilinear Equations
14:00–18:30   Room 16
Chaired by: W.V. Petryshyn

14:00 The integration of nonlinear difference equations by means of inverse spectral problems.
(133) **Yu. M. Berezansky**, Ukrainian Academy of Sciences, Ukraine.

14:45 On a new variants degree theory of mappings and problems in hydromechanics.
(134) **M.A. Efendiev**, Universitat Stuttgart, Germany.

15:30-16:00 ....Break

16:00 Quasilinear Fredholm mappings and quasilinear PDE's.
(135) **P.M. Fitzpatrick**, University of Maryland, College Park.

16:45 TBA.
(136) **W. Fushchyck**, Ukrainian Academy of Sciences, Ukraine.

17:30-17:45 ....Break

17:45 Periodic solutions of semilinear hyperbolic equations.
(137) **P.S. Milojevic**, New Jersey Institute of Technology, Newark.

Qualitative Theory of Difference Equations (cont.)
14:00–19:15   Room 6
Chaired by: R.P. Agarwal

14:00 Sign properties of Green's functions and maximum principles for difference equations.
(138) **P.W. Eloe**, University of Dayton, Dayton.

14:45 Some qualitative properties of difference systems.
(139) **L.H. Erbe**, University of Alberta, Canada.

15:30–16:00 ....**Break**

16:00 Stability and periodicity of Volterra difference equations.
(140) **S.N. Elaydi**, Trinity University, San Antonio.

16:45 Traveling waves for a class of cooperative tridiagonal systems of differential equations.
(141) **D. Hankerson**, Auburn University, Auburn.

17:30–17:45 ....**Break**

17:45 Singular boundary value problems for higher order difference equations.
(142) **J. Henderson**, Auburn University, Auburn.

18:30 TBA
(143) **B.S. Lalli***, University of Saskatchewan, Canada and **E. Thandapani**, University of Madras, India.

Blow-up, Dead Cores and Quenching (cont.)
14:00–16:45   Room 7
Chaired by: C.Y. Chan and M.K. Kwong

14:00 Conversion and penetration fronts in combustion.
(144) **I. Stakgold**, University of Delaware, Newark.

14:45 Quenching: A survey.
(145) **A. Acker**, Wichita State University, Wichita.

15:30–16:00 ....**Break**

16:00 Unbounded global solutions of a convective reaction-diffusion equation.
(146) **M. Fila**, Iowa State University, Ames.

Control Theory in Economics (cont.)
14:00–16:45   Room 8
Chaired by: E.N. Chukwu

14:00 Numerical and statistical methods in identification and control problems.
(147) **Ben G. Fitzpatrick**, University of Tennessee, Knoxville.

14:45 Two-stage optimal control problems and economic behavior.
(148) **Robert J. Rossana**, North Carolina State University, Raleigh.

15:30–16:00 ....**Break**

16:00 Dynamical systems defined by infinite horizon optimal control.
(149) **Malte Sieveking**, J.W. Goethe Universitat Frankfurt, Germany.

Structured Models in Ecology: Theory and Application
14:00–18:30   Room 14
Chaired by: T.G. Hallam and J. Cushing

14:00 A mathematical model of a plant-herbivore system.
(150) **L.S. Allen**, Texas Tech University, Lubbock.

14:45 Discrete size-structured competitive systems.
(151) **K. Crowe**, University of California, Davis.

15:30-16:00 ....**Break**

16:00 The dynamics of age-structured host-parasitoid systems.
(152) **R.M. Nisbet**, University of California, Santa Barbara.

16:45 Estimation techniques for size-structured population models.
(153) **H.T. Banks**, North Carolina State University, Raleigh.

17:30-17:45 ....**Break**

17:45 Statistical tests of fit and estimation problems for structured populations.
(154) **B. Fitzpatrick**, University of Tennessee, Knoxville.

Engineering Applications (cont.)
14:00–17:30   Room 11
Chaired by: C.R. Wimberly and R. Gibson

14:00 Application of group-theoretic techniques to nonlinear inverse problems related to stability of engineering design.
(155) **V. Komkov**, AFIT/ENC, WPAFB.

14:45 Explosion technology and wave hydrodynamics.
(156) **V.G. Korolevich**, Ukrainian Academy of Science, Ukraine.

15:30-16:00 ....**Break**

16:00 Nonlinearities at mechanical joints.
(157) **Daniel P. Hess**, University of South Florida, Tampa.

16:45 Optimization methods and stochastic analysis with applications to aerospace problems.
(158) **G.P. Svishchev**, TSAGI, Russia.

Elliptic Systems (cont.)
14:00–17:30   Room 2
Chaired by: W. Rother

14:00 A nonlinear elliptic problem with critical and subcritical Sobolev exponents.
(159) **M. Zuluaga**, Universidad Nocional Bogata D.E., Colombia.

14:45 Semilinear elliptic problems with singular potentials in R^N.
(160) **M. Badiale**, Univ. degli studi di Padova, Italy.

15:30-16:00 ....**Break**

16:00 Existence and bifurcation results for some semilinear elliptic equations on R^N.
(161) **W. Rother**, University of Bayreuth, Germany.

16:45 Genuine nonlinearity in multidimensions.
(162) **Phoolan Prasad**, Indian Institute of Science, India.

Nonlinear Operators (cont.)
14:00–17:30   Room 4
Chaired by: V. Mustonen

14:00 Degree theory for a class of semilinear mappings and applications.
(163) **V. Mustonen**, University of Oulu, Finland.

14:45 Controllability analysis of semilinear systems.
(164) **M.C. Joshi**, Indian Institute of Technology, India.

15:30-16:00 .... Break

16:00 The Newton-Kantorovich method for nonlinear integral operators.
(165) **J. Appell**, University of Wurzburg, Germany.

16:45 A nonlinear integral equation of gravimetry: Uniqueness of solution and regularization.
(166) **R. Gorenflo**, Freie Universitat, Germany.

Nonlinear Oscillations (cont.)
14:00–19:15   Room 10
Chaired by: J.R. Graef

14:00 Oscillation results for neutral differential equations.
(167) **Q. Kong**, University of Alberta, Canada.

14:45 On oscillation of nonlinear first order differential equations with its application.
(168) **H. Onose**, Ibaraki University, Japan.

15:30-16:00 .... Break

16:00 Topological and averaging approaches for nonlinear oscillations: An extension of Bhatia result.
(169) **G. Villari***, **M. Cecchi** and **M. Marini**, University of Firenze, Italy.

16:45 TBA.
(170) **M.K. Grammatikopoulos**, University of Ioannina, Greece.

17:30-17:45 .... Break

17:45 TBA.
(171) **Y. Kitamura**, Nagasaki University, Japan.

18:30 TBA.
(172) **J. Vosmansky**, Masaryk University, Czechoslovakia.

Geometric Methods (cont.)
14:00–18:30   Room 12
Chaired by: R.T. Lewis

14:00 Some applications of Peano dynamics in classical and quantum mechanics.
(173) **M.S. El Naschie**, Cornell University, Ithaca.

14:45 A nonlinear Gravito-electrodynamics: An Einsteinnien dream.
(174) **A. Yu**, Hong Kong Polytech, Hong Kong.

15:30-16:00 .... Break

16:00 Geometric spectral properties of N-body Schroedinger operators.
(175) **R.T. Lewis,** University of Alabama, Birmingham.

16:45 On realization in R^3 of two dimensional Riemannian manifolds.
(176) **H. Jiaxing,**

17:30-17:45 .... Break

17:45 Time-optimal feedback control for nonlinear systems: A geometric approach.
(177) **H. Schättler,** Washington University, St. Louis.

Parabolic Equations
14:00–19:15   Room 17
Chaired by: M. Friedman

14:00 Approximation for dissipative hereditary systems.
(178) **R.C. MacCamy,** Carnegie-Mellon University, Pittsburgh.

14:45 Solutions of the Thomas-Fermi equation for one and two dimensional lattices.
(179) **M. Friedman*, A. Rabinovitch,** and **J. Komlos,** Ben-Gurion University, Israel.

15:30-16:00 .... Break

16:00 Stability in a free boundary problem arising in the shaping of liquid.
(180) **M. Pierre,** Universite de Nancy I, France.

16:45 Stefan problems in several space variables with dynamic boundary conditions.
(181) **T. Aiki,** Nagasaki Inst. of Applied Science, Japan.

17:30-17:45 .... Break

17:45 Nonlinear diffusion equations in ground water flow and contaminant transport.
(182) **J.R. Anderson,** Ball State University, Muncie.

18:30 Decay of the step for the Kuramoto-Sivashinsky equation.
(183) **P.I. Shishmarev,** Moscow State University, Russia.

Nonlinear Waves (cont.)
14:00–18:30   Room 13
Chaired by: L. Debnath

14:00 Instabilities in integrable PDE's and their near-integrable dynamical consequences.
(184) **Greg Forest,** Ohio State University, Columbus.

14:45 On bifurcation and chaos in predator-prey systems with delay.
(185) **S. Roy Choudhury,** University of Central Florida, Orlando.

15:30-16:00 .... Break

16:00 Modified Boussinesq equations for both long and short waves.
(186) **P.L.F. Liu,** Cornell University, Ithaca.

16:45 Compressible stagnation point potential flow.
(187) **O.P. Chandna,** University of Windsor, Canada.

17:30-17:45 .... Break

17:45 Stability and instability of solitary waves.
(188) **Jerry Bona**, Pennsylvania State University, University Park.

Mathematical Modelling of Enzyme Systems
14:00–19:15   Room 18
Chaired by: R. Heinrich

14:00 Nonlinear control, nonequilibrium thermodynamics and self-organization.
(189) **Hans V. Westerhoff**, Netherlands Cancer Institute, The Netherlands.

14:45 Mathematical skeleton models of photosynthetic oscillations.
(190) **Christoph Giersch**, Technische Hochschule Darmstadt, Germany.

15:30–16:00 .... Break

16:00 Bistability in cyclic and compartmentalized enzyme systems: Irreversible transitions and spatial structures.
(191) **Jean Francois Hervagault**, Universite de Compiegne, France.

16:45 Metabolic control theory: A general theory and its applications.
(192) **Jean-Pierre Mazat***, **T. Letellier**, and **C. Reder**, Universite Bordeaux II, France.

17:30–17:45 .... Break

17:45 Mathematical models of enzyme systems: simulation, control analysis and optimization.
(193) **Reinhart Heinrich**, Humboldt Universitat, Germany.

18:30 Selection of enzymatic mechanisms which account for simplicity in the evolution of metabolic pathways.
(194) **Enrique Melendez-Hevia**, Universidad de La Laguna, Spain.

Recent Developments of Reliability Analysis and Modeling
14:00–16:45   Room 15
Chaired by: A.N.V. Rao and C.P. Tsokos

14:00 Analysis of the mean time between failure for the Weibull process.
(195) **H. Qiao and C.P. Tsokos***, University of South Florida, Tampa.

14:45 Multiple category screening procedures.
(196) **Abderrahmane Mouhab** and **Richard A. Johnson***, University of Wisconsin, Madison.

15:30–16:00 .... Break

16:00 Optimal replacement and maintenance policies for devices subject to deterioration.
(197) **Abdel Hamead**, Kuwait University, Kuwait.

Nonlinear Problems in Physics
14:00–17:30   Room B
Chaired by: E. Zeidler

14:00 Nonlinear problems in physics: Some strategies and perspectives.
(198) **E. Zeidler**, Universitat Leipzig, Germany.

14:45 Nonlinear field theories.
(199) **S. Klainerman**, Princeton University, Princeton.

15:30-16:00 .... Break

16:00 Nonsingular solutions of Einstein-Yang-Mills equations.
(200) **J. Smoller**, University of Michigan, Ann Arbor.

16:45 Unstable equilibrium configurations in differential geometry.
(201) **J. Jost**, Ruhr-Universitat Bochum, Germany.

Lyapunov Centenary Session (cont.)
13:45–19:15   Room C
Chaired by: T. Burton

13:45 Attractivity in nonautonomous equations by Lyapunov's method.
(202) **T. Yoshizawa**, Okayama University, Japan.

14:45 New directions in the method of vector Lyapunov functions via cone-valued Lyapunov functions.
(203) **A.S. Vatsala**, University of Southwestern Louisiana, Lafayette.

15:30-16:00 .... Break

16:00 On the conjecture in the Lyapunov method for functional differential equations.
(204) **Junji Kato**, Tohoku University, Japan.

16:45 Global stability of population dynamics with diffusion.
(205) **Tibor Krisztin**, Bolyai Institute, Hungary.

17:30-17:45 .... Break

17:45 On stability preserving mappings and qualitative equivalence of general dynamic systems.
(206) **A.N. Michel**, University of Notre Dame, Notre Dame.

18:30 Lyapunov functions on product spaces for integro-differential equations.
(207) **M. Rama Mohana Rao**, Indian Institute of Technology, India.

Inertial Manifolds (cont.)
14:00–17:30   Room 5
Chaired by: Roger Temam

14:00 Low-dimensional behavior in some complex geometry flows.
(208) **Yannis G. Kevrekidis,** Princeton University, Princeton.

14:45 On dynamics of some climatological equations.
(209) **Shouhong Wang,** Indiana University, Bloomington.

15:30–16:00 .... Break

16:00 Convergent families of approximate inertial manifolds.
(210) **Arnaud Debussche,** Universite de Paris-Sud, France.

16:45 Inertial manifolds and wavelets.
(211) **Olivier Goubet,** Universite de Paris-Sud, France.

Nonlinear Parabolic Problems
14:00–17:30   Room 1
Chaired by: H. Amann

14:00 Remarks on quenching.
(212) **B. Kawohl,** Universitat Heidelberg, Germany.

14:45 On the asymptotics of solutions of nonautonomous reaction-diffusion equations.
(213) **P. Hess,** University of Zurich, Switzerland.

15:30–16:00 .... Break

16:00 Geometric evolution of phase-boundaries.
(214) **Y. Giga,** Hokaido University, Japan.

16:45 Blow-up in nonlinear heat equations.
(215) **H. Matano,** University of Tokyo, Japan.

Nonsmooth Analysis and Optimization (cont.)
14:00–17:30   Room 9
Chaired by: B.S. Mordukhovich

14:00 A survey of convergence results for maximum entropy methods.
(216) **A. Lewis,** University of Waterloo, Canada.

14:45 Sensitivity analysis for generalized equations and variational inequalities.
(217) **B. Mordukhovich,** Wayne State University, Detroit.

15:30–16:00 .... Break

16:00 Inverse mapping theorems for multifunctions.
(218) **J.-P. Penot,** University of Pau, France.

16:45 Stochastic differential equations with constraints.
(219) **L. Thibault,** University of Pau, France.

Fixed Points and Related Topics (cont.)
14:00–16:45   Room 3
Chaired by: E. Fadell and A. Kirk

14:00 Nonstandard methods in metric fixed point theory.
(220) **M.A. Khamsi,** University of Texas at El Paso, El Paso.

14:45 The fixed point index and its application to differential equations.
(221) **Roger Nussbaum,** Rutgers University, New Brunswick.

15:30-16:00 .... Break

16:00 Bifurcation and the Atiyah-Singer theorem.
(222) **Jacobo Pejsachowicz,** Politechnico di Torino, Italy.

Semilinear Equations (cont.)
14:00–17:30   Room 16
Chaired by: W.V. Petryshyn

14:00 Recent development in the theory of semilinear equations.
(223) **W.V. Petryshyn,** Rutgers University, New Brunswick.

14:45 TBA.
(224) **I.V. Skrybnik,** Gust. Prikl. Mat. Mech., Ukraine.

15:30-16:00 .... Break

16:00 TBA.
(225) **J.R. Webb,** University of Glasgow, Great Britain.

16:45 TBA.
(226) **S.C. Walsh,** Southwest Texas State University, San Marcos.

Qualitative Theory of Difference Equations (cont.)
14:00–18:30   Room 6
Chaired by: R.P. Agarwal

14:00 Recent developments in the oscillation and stability of delay difference equations.
(227) **G. Ladas,** University of Rhode Island, Kingston.

14:45 A fixed point theorem for a nonlinear difference equation.
(228) **W.T. Patula,** Southern Illinois University, Carbondale.

15:30-16:00 .... Break

16:00 Disconjugacy and C-disfocality of a self-adjoint vector equation.
(229) **A. Peterson,** University of Nebraska, Lincoln.

16:45 TBA.
(230) **M. Pinto,** University of Chile, Chile.

17:30-17:45 .... Break

17:45 On the solution-like solutions of the discrete wave equations.
(231) **D. Trigiante,** Universita Degli Studi di Bari, Italy.

≡≡≡ **Periodic Solutions of Boundary Value Problems** ≡≡≡
14:00–18:30   Room 7
Chaired by: S. Ahmad and A. Lazer

14:00 Open questions and recent progress on oscillatory solutions in asymmetric.
(232) **Joe McKenna,** University of Connecticut, Storrs.

14:45 Periodic solutions for a nonlinear suspension bridge model.
(233) **Alessandro Fonda,** Institut de Mathematique, Belgium.

15:30-16:00 ....**Break**

16:00 On the problem of N competing species.
(234) **Shair Ahmad*,** The University of Texas at San Antonio, San Antonio and **Alan C. Lazer,** University of Miami, Coral Gables.

16:45 Existence of solutions of ordinary differential equations involving the p-Laplacian.
(235) **Gerhard Metzen,** Memphis State University, Memphis.

17:30-17:45 ....**Break**

17:45 Periodic stability and reachability of nonlinear parabolic equations under boundary periodic perturbations.
(236) **Koichro Naito,** Senshu University, Japan.

≡≡≡ **Mathematical Models in Combustion Theory** ≡≡≡
14:00–18:30   Room 2
Chaired by: A. Lunardi

14:00 Large time behavior of reaction-diffusion systems modeling combustion with complex chemistry.
(237) **J. Avrin,** University of North Carolina at Charlotte, Charlotte.

14:45 What do the asymptotic blow-up tell us?
(238) **J. Bebernes,** University of Colorado at Boulder, Boulder.

15:30-16:00 ....**Break**

16:00 Stability analysis of the traveling wave solutions in the burning solid propellants.
(239) **C.D. Pagani*** and **M. Verri,** Politecnico di Milano, Italy.

16:45 A free boundary problem associated with pulsating flames.
(240) **V. Roytburd*** and **M. Frankel,** Rensselaer Polytechnic Institute, Troy.

17:30-17:45 ....**Break**

17:45 Stability analysis of some traveling waves with interface conditions.
(241) **C. Schmidt-Laine*, F. Alabau, C.-M. Brauner,** and **A. Lunardi,** Ecole Normale Superieure de Lyon, France.

Mathematics and Computer Vision
14:00–17:30   Room 10
Chaired by: J.M. Morele and S. Solomini

14:00 Nonoscillatory free boundary image restoration.
(242) **Leonid Rudin**, Cognitech, Inc., Santa Monica.

14:45 A geometric model for active contours in image processing.
(243) **Francoise Dibos*** and **Francine Catte**, University of Paris IX, France.

15:30-16:00 ....**Break**

16:00 Second generation image coding and wavelet transform.
(244) **Jacques Froment***, and **Stephane Mallat**, Universite Paris-Dauphine, France.

16:45 Formalization of image segmentation in a variational framework.
(245) **Georges Koepfler**, Cognitech, Inc., Santa Monica.

Numerical Nonlinear Control and Applications
14:00–17:30   Room 8
Chaired by: K.L. Teo and T.L. Vincent

14:00 Overview of optimal trajectories for aero-assisted orbital transfer.
(246) **A. Miele**, Rice University, Houston.

14:45 Long-term planning of hydro-thermo power systems.
(247) **K.H. Wong**, University of Witswatersrand, South Africa.

15:30-16:00 ....**Break**

16:00 On the optimal drug administration of a discrete cancer chemotherapy model.
(248) **C.S. Lee***, University of Malaya, Malaysia, **V. Rehbock**, and **K.L. Teo**.

16:45 Notch filter feedback control of a chaotic system.
(249) **W.J. Grantham***, Washington State University, Pullman, and **A.M. Athalye**.

Nonlinear Aspects of the Analysis and Computations
for Microelectronic Devices "In memory of Dr. F. Odeh"
14:00–17:30   Room 11
Chaired by: T. Kerkhoven

14:00 Numerical computation of magnetic domains in pole-tips.
(250) **M. Henderson**, IBM, T.J. Watson Research Center, Yorktown Heights.

14:45 Analysis and simulation of energy transport models for semiconductors.
(251) **J. Jerome**, Northwestern University, Evanston.

15:30-16:00 ....**Break**

16:00 Nonlinearities in quantum-mechanical and drift-diffusion semiconductor models.
(252) **T. Kerkhoven**, University of Illinois at Urbana-Champaign, Urbana.

16:45 TBA.
(253) **W.M. Coughran, Jr.**, AT&T Bell Laboratories, Murray Hill.

Chaos
14:00–18:30   Room 12
Chaired by: S. Hastings

14:00 Chaos for ODE's.
(254) **S. Hastings,** University of Pittsburgh, Pittsburgh.

14:45 Partial differential equations of mixed type and chaos.
(255) **D.Y. Hsieh,** University of Science and Technology, Hong Kong.

15:30-16:00 ....Break

16:00 Chaos and complexity in two-dimensional condensed matter systems.
(256) **A. Bishop,** Los Alamos National Laboratory, Los Alamos.

16:45 Chaotic mixing and applications.
(257) **H. Yang,** The University of Chicago, Chicago.

17:30-17:45 ....Break

17:45 Chaotic systems with a Lyapunov exponent near zero may have spurious numerical trajectories.
(258) **J. Yorke,** Institute for Physical Science, College Park.

Nonlinear Operators (cont.)
14:00–17:30   Room 4
Chaired by: S. Hu

14:00 The Pareto solution of cone inequalities and application to mathematical economics.
(259) **E. Tarafdar,** McMaster University, Canada.

14:45 Nonlinear Hammerstein integral equations and integrable solutions.
(260) **G. Emmanuele,** University of Catania, Italy

15:30-16:00 ....Break

16:00 Some results on differential inclusions.
(261) **S. Hu,** Southwest Missouri State, Springfield.

16:45 Global analysis of equations with Fredholmian and set-valued operators.
(262) **Y.G. Borisovich,** Voronezh State University, Russia.

Nonlinear Inverse/Ill-Posed Problems
14:00–19:15   Room 13
Chaired by: M.Z. Nashed

14:00 Inverse problems related to integrable nonlinear partial differential equations.
(263) **P. Sabatier,** University of Montpellier II, France.

14:45 A finite difference scheme for an inverse heat equation.
(264) **John R. Cannon,** Lamar University, Beaumont.

15:30-16:00 ....Break

16:00 On the determination of potentials without bound state data.
(265) **Paul E. Sacks,** Iowa State University, Ames.

16:45 On a reconstruction procedure and some uniqueness results for multidimensional inverse spectral problems.
(266) **Yaroslav Kurylev,** St. Petersburg Branch of the Steklov Mathematical Institute, Russia and Purdue University, Lafayette, Indiana.

17:30-17:45 .... Break

17:45 (i) Nonlinear inverse problems and Carleman estimates. (ii) Phaseless inverse scattering and phase problems in optics.
(267) **Michael V. Klibanov,** University of North Carolina at Charlotte, Charlotte.

Critical Point Theory and Hamiltonian Systems
14:00–17:30   Room 14
Chaired by: D. Benci

14:00 TBA.
(268) **Eric Sere,** France.

14:45 TBA.
(269) **V. Coti Zelati,** SISSA, Italy.

15:30-16:00 .... Break

16:00 TBA.
(270) **M. Girardi,** University of L'Aquila, Italy.

16:45 TBA.
(271) **C. Viterbo,** France.

Parabolic Equations (cont.)
14:00–17:30   Room 17
Chaired by: S. Carl

14:00 Existence and multiplicity of periodic solutions for semilinear parabolic equations.
(272) **N. Hirano,** Yokohama National University, Japan.

14:45 Existence of bounded solutions for some degenerated quasilinear parabolic equations.
(273) **F. Nicolosi,** University of Catania, Italy.

15:30-16:00 .... Break

16:00 TBA
(274) **J. Saranen,** University of Oulu, Finland.

16:45 On the existence of traveling waves to reaction-diffusion systems.
(275) **K.R. Schneider,** Germany.

Mathematical Modeling of Enzyme Systems (cont.)
14:00–18:30   Room 18
Chaired by: R. Heinrich

14:00 Mathematical description of regulation in metabolic systems.
(276) **Jan-Hendrik Hofmer***, University of Stellenbosch, South Africa and **A. Cornish-Bowden**, Marseille, France.

14:45 Frequency dependency of catlyzed reactions in oscillating fields.
(277) **R. Dean Astumian*** and **B. Robertson**, National Institute of Standards and Technology, Bethesda.

15:30-16:00 .... Break

16:00 Self-activation and self-inhibition kinetics of enzymes.
(278) **Hermann-Georg Holzhutter**, Humboldt-Universitat, Germany.

16:45 Hormone-induced $[Ca^{2+}]$-oscillations in hepatocytes: Mechanism and modulation in theory and practice.
(279) **Jörg W. Stucki*** and **R. Somogyi**, Universitat Bern, Switzerland.

17:30-17:45 .... Break

17:45 Control and regulation in complex metabolic networks.
(280) **D. Kahn***, INRA-CNRS, France, **S. Schuster**,, Humboldt University and **H.V. Westerhoff.**, Netherlands Cancer Institute.

Mathematical Epidemiology
14:00–19:15   Room 15
Chaired by: C. Castillo-Chavez

14:00 Models for biased partnership formation.
(281) **Jia Li***, University of Alabama in Huntsville, Huntsville, and **J. Hyman**, Los Alamos National Laboratory, Los Alamos.

14:45 A mathematical model for AIDS in the heterosexual population: Measuring infectivity.
(282) **Denise Kirschner**, Vanderbilt University, Nashville.

15:30-16:00 .... Break

16:00 Pair formation and inherited diseases.
(283) **Stavros Busenberg***, Harvey Mudd College, Claremont, **S.P. Blythe**, University of Tennessee, Knoxville, and **C. Castillo-Chavez**, Cornell University, Ithaca.

16:45 How to conditionally complete two sex-mixing matrices with insufficient data from a survey.
(284) **Shwu-fang Shyu***, **G. Rubin**, **C. Castillo-Chavez**, Cornell University and **D. Umbach.**

17:30-17:45 .... Break

17:45 Uses of epidemiological models for food web dynamics.
(285) **Jorge X. Velasco***, Univ. Autonoma Metro. Xochimicco, Mexico, and **C. Castillo-Chavez**, Cornell University, Ithaca.

18:30 Dynamics for a class of population models with delay and diffusion effects.
(286) **Wenzhang Huang***, Georgia Institute of Technology, Atlanta, **S. Busenberg**, Harvey Mudd College, Claremont, and **K. Cooke**, Pomona College, Claremont.

Nonlinear Problems in Physics (cont.)
14:00–17:30   Room B
Chaired by: E. Zeidler

14:00 Nonlinear and chaotic fluid behavior in multi-phase mixing layers.
(287) **J. Glimm**, SUNY at Stony Brook, Stony Brook.

14:45 Global problems of nonlinear elasticity.
(288) **S. Antman**, University of Maryland, College Park.

15:30-16:00 .... **Break**

16:00 Bifurcation for variational inequalities and applications to elasticity.
(289) **F. Schuricht**, Universitat Leipzig, Germany.

16:45 Regularity for an obstacle problem in elasticity.
(290) **R. Schumann**, Universitat Leipzig, Germany.

Lyapunov's Centenary Session (cont.)
14:00–19:15   Room C
Chaired by: L. Hatvani

14:00 New directions in the method of vector Lyapunov functions.
(291) **S. Leela**, SUNY at Geneseo, Geneseo.

14:45 New approach to dynamic programming for optimal control problems with state constraints.
(292) **M.M. Khrustalev**, Moscow Aviation Institute, Russia.

15:30-16:00 .... **Break**

16:00 Method of the stability theory for singularity perturbed problems with application to dynamics.
(293) **L.K. Kuzmina**, Kazan Aviation Institute, Russia.

16:45 Comparison principle with vector Lyapunov functions for analysis logical schemes.
(294) **P.K. Kuznetsov.**

17:30-17:45 .... **Break**

17:45 Direct Lyapunov method for nonlinear stability problems of establishing motion of bodies with cavities keeping liquid.
(295) **V.V. Rumjanzev**, Computing Center of the Russian Academy of Sciences, Russia.

18:30 Some new trends in Lyapunov's second method.
(296) **C. Corduneanu**, The University of Texas at Arlington, Arlington.

Inertial Manifolds (cont.)
14:00–16:45   Room 5
Chaired by: R. Temam

14:00 TBA.
(297) **George Sell,** Army High Performance Computing Research Center, Minneapolis.

14:45 TBA.
(298) **Martine Marion,** Ecole Centrale de Lyon, France.

15:30-16:00 .... Break

16:00 TBA.
(299) **Alp Eden,** Arizona State University, Tempe.

Nonlinear Parabolic Problems (cont.)
14:00–17:30   Room 1
Chaired by: H. Amann

14:00 L^p theory for Navier-Stokes equations in an exterior domain.
(300) **T. Miyakawa,** Hiroshima University, Japan.

14:45 Uniqueness, stability, blow-up for nonlinear parabolic problems.
(301) **M. Chipot,** Univ. de Metz, UFR "MIM", France.

15:30-16:00 .... Break

16:00 Weakly nonlinear Dirichlet problems on long or thin domains.
(302) **E.N. Dancer,** University of New England, Australia.

16:45 Diffusion problems in electrochemistry.
(303) **H. Amann,** Universitat Zurich, Switzerland.

Nonlinear Problems in Physics (cont.)
14:00–17:30   Room B
Chaired by: E. Zeidler

14:00 Dynamics, bifurcation, and symmetry in mechanics.
(304) **J. Marsden,** University of Caliornia, Berkeley.

14:45 Mathematics of phase transitions.
(305) **K. Hoffmann,** University of Augsburg, Germany.

15:30-16:00 .... Break

16:00 Nonlinear stochastic partial differential equations, quantum fields, and wave propagation.
(306) **S. Albeverio,** Ruhruniversitat Bochum, Germany.

16:45 Singularities of capillary surfaces.
(307) **E. Miersemann,** University of Leipzig, Germany.

Lyapunov Centenary Session (cont.)
14:00–19:15   Room C
Chaired by: J. Kato

14:00 Logic equation and qualitative behavior of nonlinear systems.
(308) **S.N. Vassilyev,** Irkutsk Computing Center, Russia.

14:45 Converse theorems of Lyapunov's direct method for systems with delay.
(309) **A.V. Kim,** Mathematical Institute, Russia.

15:30-16:00 .... Break

16:00 Global Lyapunov method for Hopfield's neural networks with nonsymmetric weight
     matrix.
(310) **R. Jiong,** Fudan University, People's Republic of China.

16:45 Uniform asymptotic stability in functional differential equations with finite delay.
(311) **Bo Zhang,** Fayetteville State University, Fayetteville.

17:30-17:45 .... Break

17:45 Stability analysis of an HIV transmission model.
(312) **X. Liu,** University of Waterloo, Canada.

18:30 Stability of neural networks.
(313) **X. Liao,** Huazhong Normal University, People's Republic of China.

Environmental Problems
14:00–17:30   Room 2
Chaired by: G. Hetzer

14:00 Reaction-diffusion problems related to climate modeling.
(314) **P.G. Schmidt,** Auburn University, Auburn.

14:45 Nonlinear models for depletion of forestry resources: Effects of industrialization,
     pollution and population.
(315) **J.B. Shukla,** Indian Institute of Technology-Kanpur, India.

15:30-16:00 .... Break

16:00 Cellular automata models applied to the study of ventricular tachycardia and
     fibrillation.
(316) **P. Auger,** Univ. de Bourgogne, France.

16:45 Analysis of energy balance climate models. **G. Hetzer,** Auburn University,
     Auburn.

Periodic Solutions of Boundary Value Problems (cont.)
14:00–18:30   Room 7
Chaired by: S. Ahmad and A. Lazer

14:00 Homotopy index and skewproduct semiflows in nonlinear nonautonomous evolu-
     tion equations of parabolic type.
(317) **M.N. Nkashama*** and **J.R. Ward,** University of Alabama, Birmingham.

14:45 The stability and the number of periodic solutions of an analytic differential equation.
(318) **Rafael Ortega**, Universidad de Granada, Spain.

15:30-16:00 .... **Break**

16:00 Almost periodic solutions of semilinear parabolic equations.
(319) **James R. Ward, Jr.**, University of Alabama at Birmingham, Birmingham.

16:45 Periodic solutions and subharmonic solutions for a class of planar systems of Lotka-Volterra type.
(320) **Tongren Ding**, Peking University, China and **Fabio Zanolin***, Universita di Udine, Italy.

17:30-17:45 .... **Break**

17:45 Boundary value problems for impulsive integro-ordinary differential equations.
(321) **Juan J. Nieto**, Universidad de Santiago de Compostela, Spain.

Nonlinear Problems in Superconductivity
14:00–19:15   Room 6
Chaired by: M.K. Kwong, and C.Y. Chan

14:00 Some models, analysis, and computations for type-II superconductivity.
(322) **Max D. Gunzburger**, Virginia Polytechnic Institute and State University, Blacksburg.

14:45 On the time-dependent Ginzburg-Landau equations in superconductivity.
(323) **Q. Du**, Michigan State University, East Lansing.

15:30-16:00 .... **Break**

16:00 Connecting orbits between periodic solutions to the Ginzburg-Landau equation.
(324) **P. Takac**, Vanderbilt University, Nashville.

16:45 Inexact Newton methods and the Ginzburg-Landau model for type-II superconductors.
(325) **Mark Jones***, **Paul Plassmann**, and **Steve Wright**, Argonne National Laboratory, Argonne.

17:30-17:45 .... **Break**

17:45 Macroscopic models of superconductivity.
(326) **S.J. Chapman**, Stanford University, Stanford.

18:30 Dynamics of vortices in the Ginzburg-Landau equations.
(327) **E. Weinam**, Institute for Advanced Study, Princeton.

Nonsmooth Analysis and Optimization (cont.)
14:00–16:45   Room 9
Chaired by: B. Mordukhovich

14:00 Small nonconvex generalized gradients.
(328) **J.S. Treiman**, Western Michigan University, Kalamazoo.

14:45 Equivalence of extremals in different parametrizations of problems with unbounded controls.
(329) **J. Warga**, Northeastern University, Boston.

15:30-16:00 .... Break

16:00 Second order conditions for nonsmooth optimum problems with constraints.
(330) **V.M. Zeidan,** University of Waterloo, Canada.

Computational Methods for Parameter Estimation and Control
14:00—19:15   Room 3
Chaired by: T. Herdman

14:00 Numerical techniques for control and optimization.
(331) **Janet Peterson,** Virginia Polytechnic Institute and State University, Blacksburg.

14:45 Some computational methods for boundary control problems for incompressible flows.
(332) **L. Steven Hou,** Simon Fraser University, Canada.

15:30-16:00 .... Break

16:00 Boundary conditions for the numerical simulation of fluid flow.
(333) **Thomas Svobodny,** Wright State University, Dayton.

16:45 Active control of flow around a cylinder by rotation.
(334) **Yuh-Roung Ou,** Virginia Polytechnic Institute and State University, Blacksburg.

17:30-17:45 .... Break

17:45 A direct method for parameter estimation in distributed systems.
(335) **Dennis Brewer,** University of Arkansas, Fayetteville.

18:30 Parameter identification for neural systems.
(336) **Janos Turi,** University of Texas at Dallas, Richardson.

Nonlinear Fluid Mechanics
14:00—17:30   Room 16
Chaired by: L. Krishnamurthy

14:00 Fractals and multifractals in turbulence: Some puzzling questions.
(337) **Ashvin B. Chhabra,** University of Chicago, Chicago.

14:45 Attractors of bipolar and non-Newtonian viscous fluids.
(338) **Frederick Bloom,** Northern Illinois University, DeKalb.

15:30-16:00 .... Break

16:00 Nonlinear dynamics in the low Reynolds number cylinder wake.
(339) **David J. Olinger,** Worcester Polytechnic Institute, Worcester.

16:45 Thermal convection above heater porous structures.
(340) **T. Masuoka,** Kyushu Institute of Technology, Japan.

Mathematical Modeling (cont.)
14:00–17:30   Room 8
Chaired by: K.L. Teo and T.L. Vincent

14:00 The Neural Network approach to several nonlinear control problems.
(341) **C.J. Goh**, University of Western Australia, Australia.

14:45 Control parameterization approach to optimal control problems.
(342) **K.L. Teo**, University of Western Australia, Australia.

15:30-16:00 .... Break

16:00 Trajectory following algorithms of min-max optimization problems.
(343) **T.L. Vincent***, University of Arizona, **B.S. Goh**, and **K.L. Teo**, University of Western Australia.

16:45 On the usage and application of nonlinear parameter optimization software OPTIA in constrained optimal control problems.
(344) **J. Dolezal**, Czechoslovak Academy of Science, Czechoslovakia.

Topics in Nonlinear Operators and
Set-Valued Analysis: Theory and Applications
14:00–18:30   Room 14
Chaired by: M.Z. Nashed

14:00 Asymptotic cones and closed images of set-valued maps: Extensions of a theorem of Dieudonne.
(345) **Werner Oettli***, University of Mannheim, Germany and **E. Blum**, Lima.

14:45 Well-posedness and asymptotic properties of the solutions to nonlinear plate equations with multivalued boundary conditions.
(346) **Irena Lasiecka**, University of Virginia, Charlottesville.

15:30-16:00 .... Break

16:00 A theorem on sets with connected sections and some of its applications.
(347) **Biagio Ricceri**, University of Catania, Italy.

16:45 A century of variational derivatives.
(348) **Eugene P. Hamilton***, Washington College, Chestertown and **M. Zuhair Nashed**, University of Delaware, Newark.

17:30-17:45 .... Break

17:45 New hyperspace topologies in optimization and approximation.
(349) **D.V. Pai**, Indian Institute of Technology, India.

Roots of Polynomials and Systems of Polynomials
14:00–17:30   Room 10
Chaired by: D. Trigiante

13:45 Bezout theorem and complexity.
(350) **S. Smale**, University of California, Berkeley, Berkeley.

14:45 On square root iterations for finding all zeros of generalized polynomials.
(351) **L. Petkovic**, University of Nis, Yugoslavia.

15:30-16:00 ....Break

16:00 A combination of computer algebraic and numerical techniques for the computational solution of multivariate polynomial systems.
(352) **H.J. Stetter**, Inst. fur Angewandte und Num. Math. Austria.

16:45 On the computation of multiple defective eigenvalues of highly non-normal matrices.
(353) **F. Chatelin**, IBM-France, CMAP, France.

The Dynamics of Oscillatory and Excitable Biological Systems
14:00–18:30   Room 11
Chaired by: H.G. Othmer

14:00 Two-dimensional spiral waves in the heart.
(354) **Jose Jalife**, SUNY Health Sciences Center, Syracuse.

14:45 A new method for the computation of wave propagation in excitable media.
(355) **Leon Glass**, McGill University, Canada.

15:30-16:00 ....Break

16:00 Automation simulation of Turing structures in chemical and neural systems.
(356) **Mario Markus*** and **Hans Schepers**, Max Planck Institut fur Ernahrungsphysiologie, Germany.

16:45 Firefly synchronization
(357) **Steven Strogatz**, MIT, Cambridge.

17:30-17:45 ....Break

17:45 Resonance and phase-locking in forced excitable media.
(358) **H.G. Othmer**, University of Utah, Salt Lake City.

Nonlinear Inverse/Ill-Posed Problems (cont.)
14:00–17:30   Room 13
Chaired by: G. Anger

14:00 Basic principles in inverse problems.
(359) **G. Anger**, Martin Luther University, Germany.

14:45 Nonlinear ill-posed problems.
(360) **A.G. Yagola***, et al., Moscow State University, Russia.

15:30-16:00 ....Break

16:00 Obtaining optimal convergence rates for Tikhonov regularization of nonlinear ill-posed problems.
(361) **Heinz W. Engl**, Johannes-Kepler University Linz, Austria.

16:45 Newton-like methods for nonlinear inverse problems.
(362) **M. Zuhair Nashed**, University of Delaware, Newark.

Nonlinear Dynamics in Manufacturing Systems
14:00–19:15   Room 4
Chaired by: S. Meerkov

14:00 The hierarchal organization of a manufacturing system scheduler.
(363) **Stanley Gershwin,** Massachusetts Institute of Technology, Cambridge.

14:45 Dynamics scheduling of manufacturing systems.
(364) **P.R. Kumar,** University of Illinois, Urbana.

15:30-16:00 ....Break

16:00 Monotone structure and nonlinear dynamics in manufacturing systems.
(365) **David D. Yao,** Columbia University, New York.

16:45 Asymptotic analysis of production systems.
(366) **S.M. Meerkov,** University of Michigan, Ann Arbor.

17:30-17:45 ....Break

17:45 Aggregation in mathematical models of manufacturing processes.
(367) **A.A. Pervozvansky,** Leningrad State Technical University, Russia.
18:30 Clustering analysis in manufacturing systems.
(368) **A.A. Dorofeuk,** Russian Academy of Sciences, Russia.

Computational Methods
14:00–17:30   Room 12
Chaired by: J.W. Neuberger

14:00 Sobolev gradients and differential equations.
(369) **J.W. Neuberger,** North Texas State University, Denton.

14:45 A unified approach to some classes of simultaneous inclusion method for polynomial roots.
(370) **J. Herzberger,** Universitat Oldenburg, Germany.

15:30-16:00 ....Break

16:00 Roots of polynomials and systems of polynomials.
(371) **M. Sambandham,** Morehouse College and Clark Atlanta University, Atlanta.

16:45 Analytical solution of nonlinear ordinary or partial differential equations by decomposition method.
(372) **G. Adomian,** Athens.

Hyperbolic Equations
14:00–18:30   Room 17
Chaired by: R.W. Carroll

14:00 Duality and variational principles for nonlinear hyperbolic equations.
(373) **A. Nowakowski,** University of Lodz, Poland.

14:45 Decay and global existence for some nonlinear dissipative wave equations.
(374) **M. Nakao,** Kyushu University, Japan.

15:30-16:00 .... Break

16:00 Soliton theory: The tau function theme.
(375) **R.W. Carroll**, University of Illinois, Urbana.

16:45 On the global solutions to semilinear wave equations in a bounded domain.
(376) **Y. Ebihara**, Fukuoka University, Japan.

17:30-17:45 .... Break

17:45 A physically nonlinear solid with uniaxial wave propagation.
(377) **M.C. Singh**, University of Calgary, Canada.

Mathematical Epidemiology (cont.)
14:00–18:30   Room 15
Chaired by: C. Castillo-Chavez

14:00 Modeling screening and treatment programs for HIV/AIDS transmissions.
(378) **Ying-Hen Hsieh***, Cornell University, and **J.X. Velasco**, Universidad Autonoma, Metropolitana-Xochimilco, Mexico.

14:45 Modeling Antigenic Diversity, the immune system, and AIDS.
(379) **Linda Harnevo**, Barilon University, Israel.

15:30-16:00 .... Break

16:00 Infectious disease models with variable infectivity.
(380) **Fred Brauer**, University of Wisconsin, Madison.

16:45 Modeling HIV/AIDS infection with age dependence.
(381) **Xiaolong Luo**, University of Missouri, St. Louis.

17:30-17:45 .... Break

17:45 The role of social dynamics in theoretical epidemiology/biology.
(382) **C. Castillo-Chavez**, Cornell University, Ithaca.

Dynamics of Populations of Cells and Genes:
Gene Amplifications and Related Topics
14:00–17:30   Room 18
Chaired by: M. Kimmel and G. Webb

14:00 Dynamics of gene amplification and related processes.
(383) **Marek Kimmel**, Rice University, Houston.

14:45 Gene amplification by unequal chromatide exchange.
(384) **K. Baggerly**, Rice University, Houston.

15:30-16:00 .... Break

16:00 Time-continuous model of unstable gene amplification.
(385) **D. Stivers**, Rice University, Houston.

16:45 Gene amplification and drug resistance in cancer cells.
(386) **Linda Harnevo**, Barilan University, Israel.

Topological and Variational Methods in Boundary Value Problems
14:00–17:30   Room 1
Chaired by: D.G. deFigueiredo and J. Mawhin

14:00 Radial and nonradial solutions of a semilinear elliptic problem in R^n.
(387) **Th. Bartsch,** Universitat Heidelberg, Germany.

14:45 Forced oscillations on even dimensional spheres.
(388) **M. Furi,** Universita di Firenze, Italy.

15:30–16:00 .... Break

16:00 A geometric method for periodic solutions of ordinary differential equations.
(389) **R. Srzednicki,** University of Cracow, Poland.

16:45 The Conley index and nonautonomous differential equations.
(390) **J.R. Ward, Jr.,** University of Alabama, Birmingham.

Cells and Genes: Chemotherapy and Cell Dynamics
14:00–18:30   Room 18
Chaired by: M. Kimmel and G. Webb

14:00 Improving the rationale of chemotherapy: From theory of population dynamics to clinical trials.
(391) **Z. Agur,** The Weizmann Institute, Israel.

14:45 Mathematical models, numerical analysis, and computer simulation for synchronization of cell growth.
(392) **Chichia Chiu,** Michigan State University, East Lansing.

15:30–16:00 .... Break

16:00 Modeling cell colonies.
(393) **Y. Gusev,** Rutgers University, New Brunswick.

16:45 The cumulative formulation of nonlinear structured population models.
(394) **M. Gyllenberg,** Lulea University, Sweden.

17:30–17:45 .... Break

17:45 Cell population models of periodic chemotherapy.
(395) **G.F. Webb,** Vanderbilt University, Nashville.

Nonlinear Structural Mechanics Part I: Geometrically and Physically Nonlinear Problems
14:00–17:30   Room 2
Chaired by: R. Schmidt

14:00 On the numerical analysis of buckling of general thin shells.
(396) **M. Bernadou,** INRIA, France.

14:45 Random fields in nonlinear structural problems.
(397) **E. Bielewicz*, H. Walukiewica,** and **J. Gorski,** Technical University of Gdansk, Poland.

15:30-16:00 ....Break

16:00 Geometrically nonlinear analysis of inelastic shells of revolution.
(398) **D. Weichert***, Universite des Sciences et Techniques de Lille, France **R. Schmidt**, Bergische Universitat, Germany, **I. Kreja**, and **O.M.M. Teyeb**.

16:45 Moderate rotations of shells under circulatory landing.
(399) **W. Altman**, Universidade de Sao Paulo, Brazil and **A.F. Palmerio**, Instituto de Atividades Espaciais, Brazil.

Computational Methods for
Parameter Estimation and Control (cont.)
14:00–19:15   Room 3
Chaired by: T. Herdman

14:00 Numerical methods for identification of singular integro-differential equations.
(400) **Richard Fabiano**, Texas A&M University, College Station.

14:45 Parameter identification using quasilinearization.
(401) **Patricia Hammer**, Hollins College, Roanoke.

15:30-16:00 ....Break

16:00 Multi-level approach for approximating LQR problems in infinite dimensions systems.
(402) **Chunming Wang**, University of Southern California, Los Angeles.

16:45 Uniform exponential approximation to the LQR problem of thermoelastic systems.
(403) **Zhuangyi Liu**, University of Minnesota at Duluth, Duluth.

17:30-17:45 ....Break

17:45 On a mathematical model of phase transition in materials with memory.
(404) **Ruben Spies**, University of Minnesota, Minneapolis.
18:30 Control of a multiple component structure.
(405) **Belinda B. King**, North Carolina State University, Raleigh.

Nonlinear Fluid Mechanics (cont.)
14:00–17:30   Room 16
Chaired by: L. Krishnamurthy

14:00 Some problems relating to open boundaries in fluid flow.
(406) **Michael Renardy**, Virginia Tech, Blacksburg.

14:45 Direct numerical solution of transitional jet diffusion flames.
(407) **V.R. Katta**, Systems Research Laboratories, Dayton and **W.M.Roquemore***, Wright Laboratory, Wright Patterson AFB.

15:30-16:00 ....Break

16:00 Prediction of nonlinear aerodynamics for complex configurations.
(408) **L. Bruce Simpson*** and **Dave M. Belk**, Wright Laboratory, Eglin AFB.

16:45 Fluid Dynamics: Techniques in nonlinear analysis.
(409) **John M. Russel**, Florida Institute of Technology, Melbourne.

Nonlinear Controlled Systems
14:00–18:30   Room 4
Chaired by: E. Roxin

14:00 Local differential geometry and nonlinear control systems.
(410) **William Shadwick,** University of Waterloo, Canada.

14:45 Recent advances in exact linearization of nonlinear systems.
(411) **Robert Gardner,** University of North Carolina, Chapel Hill.

15:30-16:00 ....Break

16:00 Normal forms and bifurcations of control systems.
(412) **Arthur Krener,** University of California at Davis, Davis.

16:45 Nonlinear control systems and optimality.
(413) **Gianna Stefani,** Universita di Firenze, Italy.

17:30-17:45 ....Break

17:45 Geometrical methods for the analysis of the structure of optimal trajectories.
(414) **Hector Sussmann,** Rutgers University, New Brunswick.

Equations with Delay
14:00–17:30   Room 17
Chaired by: G. Ladas

14:00 Periodic and almost periodic solutions of nonlinear integral equation with delay.
(415) **R. Torrejon,** Southwest Texas State University, San Marcos.

14:45 Impulse and delay.
(416) **S.V. Krishna,** Andhra University, India.

15:30-16:00 ....Break

16:00 Survey on recent results on the asymptotic behavior of solutions to nonlinear evolution equations.
(417) **W. Rues,** Univ. Essen, Germany.

16:45 Functional-differential equations and adjoining questions of the operator theory.
(418) **M. Drakhlin,** The College of Judea and Samaria, Israel.

Topics in Nonlinear Operators and Set-Valued Analysis: Theory and Applications (cont.)
14:00–18:30   Room 14
Chaired by: M.Z. Nashed

14:00 On the steady state of infinite horizon optimal control of nonlinear control systems.
(419) **Yoshifumi Sunahara,** Kyoto Institute of Technology and Okayama University of Science, Japan.

14:45 Some stability results of vector optimization in partially ordered topological linear spaces.
(420) **E. Bednarczuk,** Systems Research Institute PAS, Poland.

15:30-16:00 ....Break

16:00 An overview of local and global inverse mapping theorems in nonlinear functional analysis.
(421) **M. Zuhair Nashed,** University of Delaware, Newark.

16:45 Global invertibility of ray-proper maps.
(422) **Jorge Hernandez,** Panama Canal College and University of Panama, Panama.

17:30-17:45 .... **Break**

17:45 Sufficient conditions for optimality.
(423) **Anthony V. Fiacco,** The George Washington University, Washington.

Roots of Polynomials and Systems of Polynomials (cont.)
14:00–16:45   Room 10
Chaired by: D. Trigiante

14:00 Fine grained and coarse grained algorithms for finding polynomial roots.
(424) **P. Fraignaud,** Lab. de l'Inform. du Parall. IMAG, France.

14:45 Solving isolated zeros polynomial systems by homotopy continuation methods.
(425) **T.Y. Li,** Michigan State University, East Lansing.

15:30-16:00 .... **Break**

16:00 Divide and conquer techniques for polynomial root finding problems.
(426) **D. Bini,** Italy.

Atmospheric and Oceanic Sciences
14:00–18:30   Room 5
Chaired by: M.P. Singh and S. Raman

14:00 Parameterization of coastal atmospheric boundary layer.
(427) **K. Sen Gupta,** Vikram Sarabhai Space Centre, India.

14:45 A review of the role of radiation transfer in the development of meso-scale circulations.
(428) **Martin Leach*** and **Sethu Raman,** North Carolina State University, Raleigh.

15:30-16:00 .... **Break**

16:00 Effects of critical level in atmospheric shear flows with thermal forcing.
(429) **Yuh-Lang Lin,** North Carolina State University, Raleigh.

16:45 Nonlinear problems in atmospheric transport and diffusions: Meso-scale modeling.
(430) **Ron Meyers,** U.S. Army Atmospheric Science Laboratory, White Sands Missile Range.

17:30-17:45 .... **Break**

17:45 Simulation and short range prediction of Asian summer monsoon circulation with a nonlinear multilevel weather prediction model.
(431) **N. Natarajan,** IAF Meteorological Directorate, India.

Nonlinear Volterra Equations
14:00–18:30   Room 6
Chaired by: S.O Londen

14:00 Finite dimensional robust control of a viscoelastic rod.
(432) **Robert L. Wheeler,** Virginia Tech, Blacksburg.

14:45 A semigroup approach to a viscoelastic Volterra equation.
(433) **O. Staffans,** Helsinki University of Technology, Finland.

15:30-16:00 .... Break

16:00 Counterexamples in the theory of abstract Volterra equations.
(434) **Wolfgang Desch,** University of Graz, Austria.

16:45 Sum of monotone operators and nonlinear Volterra equations.
(435) **Philippe Clement,** Technological University of Delft, The Netherlands.

17:30-17:45 .... Break

17:45 On some nonlinear parabolic integrodifferential equations.
(436) **Stig-Olof Londen,** Helsinki University of Technology, Finland.

Bursting Rhythms and Complex Oscillations in
Biological Systems
14:00–18:30   Room 7
Chaired by: C.D. Thron

14:00 A simple dynamical system for subthreshold oscillations in thalamic neurons.
(437) **James L. Hindmarsh,** University of Wales College of Cardiff, United Kingdom.

14:45 Stability and asymptotic analyses for polynomial bursters.
(438) **Mark Pernarowski,** University of British Columbia, Canada.

15:30-16:00 .... Break

16:00 Diffusive coupling in insulin secreting cells.
(439) **Arthur Sherman,** National Institute of Health, Bethesda.

16:45 Geometric analysis of bursting oscillations in excitable membrane models.
(440) **David Terman,** Ohio State University, Columbus.

17:30-17:45 .... Break

17:45 Models of the periodic rhythm caused by veratramine in the cardiac pacemaker.
(441) **C. Dennis Thron,** Dartmouth Medical School, Hanover.

Evolution Equations
14:00–17:30   Room 8
Chaired by: N. Kenmochi and S. Oharu

14:00 Limit of nonlinear evolution equations.
(442) **Ph. Benilan,** Universite de Franche-Comte, France.

14:45 A nonlinear systems for phase change with dissipation.
(443) **A. Damlamian,** Ecole Polytechnique, France.

15:30-16:00 .... Break

16:00 Behavior of solutions to evolution equations.
(444) **R.H. Martin, Jr.,** North Carolina State University, Raleigh.

16:45 Coupled field models in phase transitions dynamics.
(445) **M. Niezgodka,** Warsaw University, Poland

Nonlinear Stochastic Systems
14:00–17:30   Room 15
Chaired by: A.N.V. Rao and C.P. Tsokos

14:00 Limit theorems for dependent random variables.
(446) **Robert L. Taylor,** University of Georgia, Athens.

14:45 Stability of competitive-cooperative processes under random structural perturbations.
(447) **G.S. Ladde,** University of Texas at Arlington, Arlington.

15:30-16:00 .... Break

16:00 The stochastic zero-sum differential games with measurement uncertainties.
(448) **K.M. Ramachandran,** University of South Florida, Tampa.

16:45 Mixing limit theorems related to the invariance principle and their convergence rates.
(449) **Ibrahim A. Ahmad,** Northern Illinois University, DeKalb.

Computational Methods (cont.)
14:00–17:30   Room 12
Chaired by: R.E. Mickens

14:00 Dynamical systems arising from least squares completions of differential algebraic equations.
(450) **S.L. Campbell,** North Carolina State University, Raleigh.

14:45 WKB procedures for discrete Schrodinger type differential equations.
(451) **R.E. Mickens,** Clark Atlanta University, Atlanta.

15:30-16:00 .... Break

16:00 Computational methods for global analysis of homoclinic and heteroclinic orbits.
(452) **Mark J. Friedman,** University of Alabama in Huntsville, Huntsville.

16:45 Solution of Navier-Stokes equations by the decomposition model.
(453) **G. Adomian,** Athens.

Global Bifurcations and Chaos
14:00–17:30   Room 9
Chaired by: K. Gopalsamy

14:00 Heteroclinic orbits in singular systems: A unifying approach.
(454) **Flavioni Battelli,** Istituto di Biomathematica, Italy.

14:45 The progressive singular perturbation and its applications in mathematical modelling.
(455) **Bo Deng,** University of Nebraska, Lincoln.

15:30-16:00 .... Break

16:00 Twisted and nontwisted bifurcations induced by diffusion.
(456) **Xiao Bao Lin,** North Carolina State University, Raleigh.

16:45 Shadowing theorems of ODE's.
(457) **Ken Palmer,** University of Miami, Coral Gables.

Fixed Point Theory
14:00–18:30   Room 11
Chaired by: S. Heikkila

14:00 Monotone methods in nonlinear analysis.
(458) **S. Heikkila,** University of Oulu, Finland.

14:45 Spherical algorithms and evaluation of the fixed point set.
(459) **E.A. Galperin,** Univ. du Quebec a Montreal, Canada.

15:30-16:00 ....Break

16:00 Minimization theorems and fixed point theorems.
(460) **W. Takahashi,** Tokyo Institute of Technology, Japan.

16:45 Fixed points of acyclic maps on topological vector spaces.
(461) **S. Park,** Seoul National University, Korea.

17:30-17:45 ....Break

17:45 Lefschetz-Hopf-Granas fixed point theorem for noncompact spaces.
(462) **V. Okhezin,** Urals State University, Russia.

Poincare's Session
14:00–17:30   Room 13
Chaired by: C. Corduneanu

14:00 Henry Poincare: The founder of Nonlinear Analysis.
(463) **F. Browder,** Rutger's University, New Brunswick.

14:45 Qualitative behavior of bifurcating cycles and tori from an equilibrium.
(464) **S. Bernfeld,** University of Texas at Arlington, Arlington.

15:30-16:00 ....Break

16:00 TBA.
(465) **C. Corduneanu,** University of Texas at Arlington, Arlington.

16:45 Poincare and Lyapunov: A centennial legacy in ordinary differential equations.
(466) **J. Mawhin,** Univ. Cath. de Louvain, Belgium.

Nonlinear Problems in Physics (cont.)
14:00–16:45   Room B
Chaired by: E. Zeidler

14:00 Capillary surfaces.
(467) **R. Finn,** Stanford University, Stanford.

14:45 Multipolar viscous fluids.
(468) **J. Necas,** Math Institute of the Czechoslovakian Academy of Science, Czechoslovakia.

15:30-16:00 .... Break

16:00 A new approach to the Navier-Stokes equations.
(469) **R. Bohme,** Ruhr-Universitat Bochum, Germany.

Lyapunov's Centenary Session (cont.)
14:00–19:15   Room C
Chaired by: V.M. Matrosov

14:00 Robust stability and quasi-monotonicity on cones via Lyapunov functions.
(470) **S. Sivasundaram,** Embry-Riddle Aeronautical University, Daytona Beach.

14:45 Stability and attractivity theorems for ODE's and FDE's by Lyapunov's Direct Method.
(471) **L. Hatvani,** Bolyai Institute, Hungary.

15:30-16:00 .... Break

16:00 Stability and attraction in impulsive semidynamical systems.
(472) **S.K. Kaul,** University of Regina, Canada.

16:45 The correlation between vibrations and buckling of imperfect stiffened shells.
(473) **Josef Singer,** Technion-Israel Institute of Technology, Israel.

17:30-17:45 .... Break

17:45 A unifying approach to Lyapunov's direct method: Generic stability concepts and subsidiary parametric function method.
(474) **Vladimir B. Bajic,** Belgrade, Yugoslavia.
18:30 A universal integral invariant of non-autonomous dynamical systems.
(475) **Veljko Vujicic,** Matematicki Institut, Yugoslavia.

Bifurcation
14:00–17:30   Room 6
Chaired by: S.R. Bernfeld

14:00 Homoclinic bifurcation from degenerate singularities.
(476) **R.I. Becker,** University of Cape Town, South Africa.

14:45 Bifurcation control of stressed nonlinear systems.
(477) **E.H. Abed,** University of Maryland, College Park.

15:30-16:00 ....Break

16:00 Bifurcation analysis of non-uniform flow patterns in axial flow gas compressors.
(478) **R.A. Adomaitis,** University of Maryland, College Park.

16:45 Hopf bifurcation in energy-balance climate models.
(479) **P.G. Schmidt,** Auburn University, Auburn.

Topological and Variational Methods in Nonlinear Boundary Value Problems (cont.)
14:00–17:30   Room 1
Chaired by: D.G. deFigueiredo and J. Mawhin

14:00 Non-ordered upper and lower solutions in semilinear elliptic problems.
(480) **J.P. Gossez,** Universite Libre de Bruxelles, Belgium.

14:45 Index at infinity and application to nonlinear boundary value problems.
(481) **A.M. Krasnosel'skii,** Institute for Information Transmission Problems, Russia.

15:30-16:00 ....Break

16:00 Boundary value problems for superlinear differential equations.
(482) **B. Ruf,** Universita di Milano, Italy.

16:45 A morse theory for strongly indefinite functionals with applications.
(483) **A. Szulkin,** Stockholm University, Sweden.

Nonlinear Structural Mechanics
Part 2: Composite Materials and Structures
14:00–16:45   Room 2
Chaired by: R. Schmidt

14:00 Further results concerning the post-buckling behavior of composite laminated shallow structures taking into account initial geometric imperfections.
(484) **L. Librescu*** and **M.Y. Chang,** Virginia Politechnic Institute and State University, Blacksburg.

14:45 Failure prediction in composite laminates according to the layer-wise plate theory.
(485) **J.N. Reddy*** and **Y.S.N. Reddy,** Virginia Politechnic Institute and State University, Blacksburg.

15:30-16:00 ....Break

16:00 Nonlinear static and transient analysis of composite laminates.
(486) **R. Schmidt,** Bergische Universitat, Germany.

Multiple Solutions of
Nonlinear Differential Equations
14:00–17:30   Room 3
Chaired by: K.C. Chang

14:00 TBA.
(487) **H. Hofer**, Ruhr Universitat Bochum, Germany.

14:45 TBA.
(488) **Z.C. Han**, Stanford University, Stanford.

15:30–16:00 .... Break

16:00 TBA.
(489) **J.W. Liu**, Academy of Science, China.

16:45 TBA.
(490) **K. Schmitt**, University of Utah, Salt Lake City.

Math Modelling of Cellutor Interaction Dynamics
with Special Emphasis on Immune Systems Mechanics
14:00–17:30   Room 9
Chaired by: S.I. Andersson

14:00 Nonlinear analysis of stability, oscillations and control of immunological processes
(491) **V.M. Matrosov**, Russian Academy of Sciences, Russia.

14:45 TBA.
(492) **Christiane A. Helm**, Universitat Mainz, Germany.

15:30–16:00 .... Break

16:00 Mathematical modelling of cellular interactin dynamics of multicellular tumor speroids.
(493) **Zeljko Bajzer**, Mayo Clinic, Rochester.

16:45 A dynamical systems approach to the IL-2 receptor complex.
(494) **Stig I. Andersson**, Research Group of Global Analysis and Applications, Sweden.

Neural Networks: Algorithms and Applications
14:00–18:30   Room 4
Chaired by: D. Lainiotis

14:00 Polynomials networks for optimal nonlinear filtering.
(495) **James Ting-Ho Lo*** and **Melvin J. Sanders**, The University of Maryland, Baltimore.

14:45 Neural net architecture for model-reference adaptive control: Stability and convergence.
(496) **David C. Hyland*** and **James A. King**, Harris Corporation, Palm Bay.

15:30–16:00 .... Break

16:00 Computational characteristics of adaptive resonance theory Neural Nets.
(497) **Laurene Fausett***, Florida Institute of Technology, Melbourne.

16:45 Differentiating and pruning multilayer feed-forward neural networks.
(498) **James Ting-Ho Lo***, and **Lei Yu**, University of Maryland, Baltimore.

17:30-17:45 .... Break

17:45 Convergence and stability analysis of neural networks using vector Lyapunov functions.
(499) **D.W. Fausett***, Florida Institute of Technology, Melbourne and **S. Koksal**, University of Southwestern Louisiana, Lafayette.

Methods of Nonconvex Analysis
14:00–18:30   Room 16
Chaired by: A. Cellina

14:00 TBA.
(500) **A. Bressan**, Universita di Padova, Italy.

14:45 TBA.
(501) **P. Marcellini**, Dipt. Matematico "U. Dini", Italy.

15:30-16:00 .... Break

16:00 TBA.
(502) **G. Pianigiani**, Universita de Siena, Italy.

16:45 TBA
(503) **A. Cellina**, SISSA, Italy.

17:30-17:45 .... Break

17:45 TBA
(504) **A.A. Tolstonogov**, Irkutsk Computing Center, Russia.

Hereditary Systems and Their Application
14:00–18:30   Room 7
Chaired by: V. Kolmanovskii

14:00 Linear asymptotically autonomous neutral functional differential equations with multiple eigenvalues.
(505) **A.F. Ize**, ICMSC-USR, Brazil.

14:45 Models of diffusing population in patchy environments.
(506) **H.I. Freedman**, University of Alberta, Canada.

15:30-16:00 .... Break

16:00 Optimal stabilization of controlled systems with random structure.
(507) **I.Ja. Katz**, Mathematical Institute, Russia.

16:45 Converse theorems of Lyapunov direct method for systems with delay.
(508) **A.V. Kim**, Mathematical Institute, Russia.

17:30-17:45 .... Break

17:45 Optimal control and estimate of stochastic hereditary systems.
(509) **V.B. Kolmanovskii**, Moscow, Russia.

Atmospheric and Oceanic Sciences (cont.)
14:00–18:30   Room 5
Chaired by: M.P. Singh and S. Raman

14:00 Energy transfers in gulf stream frontal instabilities: Model and observations.
(510) **Leonard J. Pieirafesa, Leangchwan C. Sun*, and Gerald S. Janowitz,** North Carolina State University, Raleigh.

14:45 Turbulence structure in the atoms, boundary layer-data and models.
(511) **K.S. Rao,** NOAA/Atmospheric Turbulence and Diffusion Laboratory, Oak Ridge.

15:30–16:00 ....**Break**

16:00 A review of ocean-atmosphere coupled models with special emphasis on meso-scale processes.
(512) **Sethu Raman and Neeraja Reddy*,** North Carolina State University, Raleigh.

16:45 Review of recent advances in the development of semi-Lagrangian numerical models in meteorology.
(513) **Fredrick H.M. Semazzi,** North Carolina State University, Raleigh.

17:30–17:45 ....**Break**

17:45 An analytical study of diurnal wind-structure variations in the boundary-layer and the low level nocturnal jet.
(514) **M.P. Singh,** Indian Institute of Technology, India.

Stability Problems in Nonlinear
Compartmental Systems with Pipes and Delays
14:00–17:30   Room 11
Chaired by: I. Gyori

14:00 TBA.
(515) **Jianhong Wu,** Universite York, Canada.

14:45 TBA.
(516) **Tibor Krisztin,** Bolyan Institute Univer. of Szeged, Hungary.

15:30–16:00 ....**Break**

16:00 TBA.
(517) **Claudio Cobelli,** Univ. of Padova, Italy.

16:45 TBA.
(518) **H.I. Freedman,** University of Alberta, Canada.

Deterministic Control of Uncertain Systems
14:00–18:30   Room 12
Chaired by: M. Corless

14:00 Stability of a class of nonlinear singularly perturbed systems that contain marginally stable boundary layers.
(519) **D. Da and M. Corless*,** Purdue University, W. Lafayette.

14:45 Positive definiteness of quadratic forms over polytopes: Applications to the robust stability problem.
(520) **F. Garofalo, L. Glielmo and L. Verde,** University of Naples, Italy.

15:30–16:00 ....Break

16:00 Universal stabilizers for classes of nonliner systems.
(521) **E.P. Ryan**, University of Bath, United Kingdom.

16:45 Stabilization of uncertain systems using discontinuous control.
(522) **S.E. Rebiai** and **A.S.I. Zinober**, University of Sheffield, United Kingdom.

17:30–17:45 ....Break

17:45 Simultaneous stabilizatin of a family of SISO nonlinear systems via output feed-back control.
(523) **A. Saberi** and **Z. Lin***, Washington State University, Pullman.

Accretive and Monotone Operator Theory
14:00–19:15   Room 10
Chaired by: A.G. Kartsatos

14:00 Approximation and convergence of nonlinear semigroups.
(524) **Simeon Reich**, University of Southern California, Los Angeles.

14:45 On the range of sums of accretive and continuous operators in Banach spaces.
(525) **Claudio H. Morales**, The University of Alabama in Huntsville, Huntsville.

15:30–16:00 ....Break

16:00 Solvability of nonlinear equations involving perturbations of maximal monotone operators.
(526) **Zhengyuan Guan**, University of Wisconsin, Eau Claire.

16:45 Recent results involving compact perturbations and compact resolvents of accretive operators in Banach spaces.
(527) **Athanassios G. Kartsatos**, University of South Florida, Tampa.

17:30–17:45 ....Break

17:45 Braess' paradox and power-law nonlinearities in networks II.
(528) **Bruce D. Calvert**, University of Auckland, New Zealand.

18:30 Regular operator approximation theory.
(529) **Ram Verma**, University of Central Florida, Orlando.

Evolution Equations (cont.)
14:00–17:30   Room 8
Chaired by: N. Kenmochi and S. Oharu

14:00 Nonlinear evolution operators: Generation theory and applications.
(530) **S. Oharu***, Hiroshima University, Japan and **Y. Kobayashi**, Niiggata University, Japan.

14:45 Asymptotic stability of nonlinear evolution systems of time-dependent subdifferentials.
(531) **M. Otani**, Waseda University, Japan and **N. Kenmochi***, Chiba University, Japan.

15:30–16:00 ....Break

16:00 Nonlinear evolution equations without energy.
(532) **G. Ponce**, University of California, Santa Barbara.

16:45 A class of nonlocal nonlinear evolution problems.
(533) **J.F. Rodrigues**, CMAF/INIC and University of Lisbon, Portugal.

Problems in Hysteresis
14:00–18:30   Room 14
Chaired by: L. Tavernini and A. Visintin

14:00 Operator approaches to the investigation of systems with hysteresis.
(534) **M.A. Krasnosel'skii**, Russian Academy of Science, Russia.

14:45 Hysteresis operators, differential equations and memory.
(535) **M. Brokate**, Universitat Kaiserslautern, Germany.

15:30-16:00 .... Break

16:00 Large time behavior of solutions to hyperbolic equations with hysteresis.
(536) **P. Krejci**, CSAV, Czechoslovakia.

16:45 Preisach model with stochastic input and aftereffect.
(537) **I.D. Mayergoyz**, University of Maryland-College Park, College Park.

17:30-17:45 .... Break

17:45 Smooth solutions for a thermodynamically consistent phase- field model.
(538) **J. Spreckels**, Univ. GH Essen, Germany.

Differential Delay Equations and
Applications in Biology and Medicine
14:00–17:30   Room 13
Chaired by: U. an der Heiden

14:00 Inertial effects on the dynamics of delayed neuro-muscular feedback mechanisms.
(539) **John G. Milton*** and **Toru Ohira**, University of Chicago Hospitals, Chicago.

14:45 Higher order delay-differential equations with biomedical applications.
(540) **Uwe an der Heiden**, University of Witten/Herdecke, Germany.

15:30-16:00 .... Break

16:00 Oscillations in a delayed feedback model for motor control.
(541) **Jacques Belair**, University of Montreal, Canada.

16:45 Bifurcations and traveling waves in a delayed partial differential equation.
(542) **Michael C. Mackey**, McGill University, Canada.

Nonlinear Stochastic Systems (cont.)
14:00–18:30   Room 15
Chaired by: A.N.V. Rao and C.P. Tsokos

14:00 Stochastic control of maintained systems operating in a random environment.
(543) **Martin A. Wortman***, Texas A&M University and **Georgia Ann Klutke**, The University of Texas at Austin, Austin.

14:45 On certain nonlinear difference and differential equations arising from optimal choice problems.
(544) **Z. Govindaraulu,** University of Kentucky, Lexington.

15:30-16:00 .... Break

16:00 Optimal control of stochastic systems under constraints.
(545) **A.N.V. Rao* and Chris P. Tsokos,** University of Florida, Tampa.

16:45 Stability analysis of a class of stochastic bilinear systems.
(546) **Philip Wang* and A.N.V. Rao,** University of South Florida, Tampa.

17:30-17:45 .... Break

17:45 Models and problems on the optimal maintenance of system and control of arrivals in queue
(547) **Michael N. Katchakis,** Rutgers University, New Brunswick.

Stochastic Systems
14:00–18:30   Room 17
Chaired by: E. Dshalalow

14:00 Spacial random marked point process and random point graphs, their question, analysis, statistics, and application.
(548) **Dieter Köenig,** Berg Akademie Freiberg, Germany.

14:45 Existence of solutions of nonlinear stochastic differential inclusions on Banach spaces.
(549) **N.U. Ahmed,** University of Ottawa, Canada.

15:30-16:00 .... Break

16:00 Large deviation problem for some semilinear parabolic Ito equations.
(550) **P.L. Chow,** Wayne State University, Detroit.

16:45 Discrete dynamic systems.
(551) **D. Yadav,** Indian Institute of Technology, India.

17:30-17:45 .... Break

17:45 Asymptotic flatness of the N-point motion of the brownian flow of homeomorphism.
(552) **D. Kannan,** University of Georgia, Athens.

Optimization and Optimal Control
14:00–17:30   Room 18
Chaired by: N.U. Ahmed

14:00 Two norm approach to stability and sensitivity analysis of solutions to optimizations and optimal control problems.
(553) **K. Malanowski,** Systems Research Institute of the Polish Academy, Poland.

14:45 On nonlinear minimum norm problems in optimal control theory.
(554) **W. Krabs,** Tech. Hochschule Darmstadt, Germany.

15:30-15:45 .... Break

15:45 Generalization of the Lusternik theorem and their applications to nonsmooth and abnormal problems in optimization and optimal control.
(555) **U. Ledzewicz,** Southern Illinois University, Edwardsville.

16:30 Optimal control problems with two-point boundary conditions of anti-periodic type, via co-semigroups and normal cones.
(556) **N. Pavel,** Ohio University, Athens.

General
14:00–18:30   Room C
Chaired by: P. Rabier

14:00 Singularities in differential algebraic equations.
(557) **P. Rabier,** University of Pittsburgh, Pittsburgh.

14:45 Motion of polyhedral surfaces by crystalline curvature.
(558) **Jean E. Taylor,** Rutgers University, New Brunswick.

15:30-16:00 .... Break

16:00 Application of infinite matrices to Walsh functions.
(559) **Mursaleen,** Aligarh Muslim University, India.

16:45 Two parameter problems for the p-Laplacian.
(560) **Paul Binding,** University of Calgary, Canada.

17:30-17:45 .... Break

17:45 On rotating black holes in equilibrium in general relativity.
(561) **G. Weinstein,** University of Alabama at Birmingham, Birmingham.

Control Systems
14:00–17:30   Room B
Chaired by: D. Siljak

14:00 A block-parallel Newton's method via overlapping epsilon decompositions.
(562) **D.D. Siljak,** Santa Clara University, Santa Clara.

14:45 Asymptotic properties for a class of infinite dimensional systems.
(563) **V.M. Popov,** University of Florida, Gainesville.

15:30-16:00 .... Break

16:00 TBA.
(564) **R. Triggiani,** University of Virginia, Charlottesville.

16:45 Output tracking of non-analytic trajectories for nonlinear systems.
(565) **L.R. Hunt,** University of Texas at Dallas, Richardson.

Topological and Variational Methods in Nonlinear Boundary Value Problems (cont.)
14:00–16:45   Room 1
Chaired by: D.G. deFigueiredo and J. Mawhin

14:00 Subquadratic versus superquadratic variational problems.
(566) **D. Costa,** Universidade de Basilia, Brazil.

14:45 Semilinear discontinuous elliptic problems.
(567) **J.V.A. Goncalves,** Universidad de Brasilia, Brazil.

15:30-16:00 .... Break

16:00 TBA.
(568) **E. Mitidieri,** Universita di Trieste, Italy.

Cononical Nonlinear Modeling with Applications to Biochemical Systems
14:00–18:30   Room 8
Chaired by: M.A. Savageau

14:00 The power-law formalism: A cononical nonlinear approach to modeling and analysis.
(569) **M.A. Savageau,** The University of Michigan, Ann Arbor.

14:45 S-system analysis of the TCA cycle in Dictyostelium discoideum.
(570) **F. Shiraishi,** Kyushu Institute of Technology, Japan.

15:30-16:00 .... Break

16:00 A monomial-based version of Newton's method: Special properties and new developments.
(571) **S.A. Burns,** University of Illinois, Urbana.

16:45 Estimating S-system parameters and assessing regulatory patterns within intact biochemical pathways.
(572) **A. Sorribas*** and **M. Cascante,** Universitat de Barcelona, Spain.

17:30-17:45 .... Break

17:45 How many variables? On the dimensionality of nonlinear systems.
(573) **E.O. Voit,** Medical University of South Carolina, Charleston.

Neural Networks: Algorithms and Applications (cont.)
14:00–17:30   Room 4
Chaired by: D. Lainiotis

14:00 Neural network approach to optimal filtering.
(574) **James Ting-Ho Lo*** and **Lei Yu,** University of Maryland-Baltimore County, Baltimore.

14:45 Dynamical neural networks: Efficient training algorithms.
(575) **D.G. Lainiotis,*** K. Plataniotis, and C. Charalambous, Florida Institute of Technology, Melbourne.

15:30-16:00 .... Break

16:00 Signal recognition using a dynamic time warping neural network. using vector Lyapunov functions.

(576) **N. Tepedelenlioglu***, Florida Institute of Technology, Melbourne and **F. Unal**, Siemens Stromberg-Carlson, Boca Raton.

16:45 Efficient neural network initialization procedures.

(577) **D.G. Lainiotis***, **K. Plataniotis**, and **C. Charalambous**, Florida Institute of Technology, Melbourne.

Nonlinear Fluid Mechanics (cont.)
14:00–16:45   Room 16
Chaired by: L. Krishnamurthy

14:00 Finite amplitude cellular double diffusive steady convection with an imposed magnetic field.

(578) **I.S. Shivakumara**, Bangalore University, India

14:45 laminar and turbulent film flows.

(579) **R.J. Gribben**, University of Brunei, Brunei.

15:30-16:00 .... Break

16:00 Sensitivity equations for the $k - \epsilon$ turbulence model for ill-posed inverse problems in computational fluid dynamics.

(580) **L. Krishnamurthy**, Florida Institute of Technology, Melbourne.

Multiple Solutions of Nonlinear
Differential Equations (cont.)
14:00–17:30   Room 3
Chaired by: K.C. Chang

14:00 TBA.

(581) **Z.Q. Wang**, Utah State University, Logan.

14:45 TBA.

(582) **Y.Y. Li**, Rutgers University, New Brunswick.

15:30-16:00 .... Break

16:00 TBA.

(583) **K.C. Chang**, Peking University, People's Republic of China.

16:45 Uniqueness of solutions of nonlinear Dirichlet problems.

(584) **P.N. Srikanth**, C.I.T. Campus, India.

Neural Networks in Biomedicine
14:00–18:30   Room 2
Chaired by: N. DeClaris

14:00 Theory and biomedical applications of higher order nonlinear neural networks.

(585) **Nicholas DeClaris**, University of Maryland, Baltimore.

14:45 Neural mechanisms for object representation and recognition.

(586) **E. Micheli-Tzanakou**, Rutgers University, New Brunswick.

15:30-16:00 .... Break

16:00 Modelling the cerebellum as a neurocontroller.
(587) **P. Werbos**, National Science Foundation, Washington and **A. Pellionisz**, NASA Ames Research Center, Washington.

16:45 Neural network application for learning with large medical databases.
(588) **G. Carpenter** and **J. Reynolds***, Boston University, Boston.

17:30-17:45 ....**Break**

17:45 An application of neural networks to the study of a biochemical threshold-logic device.
(589) **M. Okamoto***, **Y. Maki** and **T.Sekiguchi**, Kyushu Institute of Technology, Japan.

Hereditary Systems and Their Application (cont.)
14:00–18:30   Room 7
Chaired by: V. Kolmanovskii

14:00 Application of functional-differential equations for modelling of lipid (fats) metabolism in human organism.
(590) **V.A. Kolosov**, ADIS Laboratory, Russia.

14:45 Some problems of qualitative theory of functional differential equations.
(591) **A.D. Myshkis**, Moscow, Russia

15:30-16:00 ....**Break**

16:00 Lyapunov method for degenerate functions and functionals.
(592) **V.R. Nosov**, MIEM, Russia.

16:45 Optimal control and estimate of stochastic hereditary systems.
(593) **L.E. Shaikhet**, Donetzk, Ukraine.

17:30-17:45 ....**Break**

17:45 Intrinsic delay, forced delay and quasi delay in physical systems.
(594) **N. McDonald**, University of Glasgow, Scotland.

Atmospheric and Oceanic Sciences (cont.)
14:00–17:30   Room 5
Chaired by: M.P. Singh and S. Raman

14:00 Review of non-hydrostatic numerical models for atmosphere.
(595) **Liang Xu, Sethu Raman***, North Carolina State University, Raleigh and **Rao V. Madala**, Naval Research Laboratory, Washington.

14:45 Chaos application in the atmosphere.
(596) **Xubin Zeng** and **Roger A. Pielke**, Colorado State University, Fort Collins.

15:30-16:00 ....**Break**

16:00 The stagnant flow upstream of hills or mountains.
(597) **K. Kitabayashi**, National Institute of Resources and Environment, Japan.

16:45 Atmospheric dispersion of lead due to traffic.
(598) **P. Goyal**, Indian Institute of Technology, India.

Stability Problems in Nonlinear Compratmental Systems with Pipes and Delays
14:00–16:45   Room 11
Chaired by: I. Gyori

14:00 Almost periodic solutions of nonlinear compartmental systems.
(599) **H. Maeda***, **T. Takahashi**, and **S. Kodama**, Osaka University, Japan.

14:45 On numerical solutions for a class of nonlinear delay equations with state and time-dependent delays.
(600) **Janos Turi***, The University of Texas at Dallas, **I. Gyori** and **F. Hartung**, Albert Szent-Gyorgyi Medical University, Hungary.

15:30-16:00 .... Break

16:00 Asymptotic stability results in delay differential equations arising in compartmental models.
(601) **Istvan Gyori**, Szent-Gyorgyi Medical University, Hungary.

Nonlinear Partial Differential Equations and Nonlinear Waves
14:00–17:30   Room 9
Chaired by: T.T. Li

14:00 TBA.
(602) **Chao-hao Gu**, University of Science and Technology, People's Republic of China.

14:45 TBA.
(603) **D. Serre**, Ecole Normale Superieure de Lyon, France.

15:30-16:00 .... Break

16:00 TBA.
(604) **W. Strauss**, Brown University, Providence.

16:45 TBA.
(605) **Jia-xing Hong**, Fudan University, People's Republic of China.

Nonlinear Stochastic Systems (cont.)
14:00–17:30   Room 15
Chaired by: A.N.V. Rao and C.P. Tsokos

14:00 On nonparametric density estimation.
(606) **H. Qiao*** and **Chris P. Tsokos**, University of South Florida, Tampa.

14:45 Smoothing splines for nonparametric regression percentiles.
(607) **Yanhua Wang**, University of Toronto, Canada.

15:30-16:00 .... Break

16:00 Asymptotic optimality of a sequential procedure for estimation.
(608) **Kamel Rekab**, Florida Institute of Technology, Melbourne.

16:45 TBA
(609) **Ibrahim A. Ahmad**, Northern Illinois University, DeKalb.

Accretive and Monotone Operator Theory (cont.)
14:00–18:30   Room 10
Chaired by: A.G. Kartsatos

14:00 On the invertability of $B + e^{-TA}$ with A and B maximal monotone operators in Hilbert space.
(610) **Nicolae Pavel,** Ohio University, Athens.

14:45 A global existence theorem on nonlinear evolution equations.
(611) **Yuncheng You,** University of South Florida, Tampa.

15:30-16:00 .... Break

16:00 Existence of solutions of nonlinear functional differential equations in L^p Spaces.
(612) **Ki Sik Ha,** Pusan National University, Korea.

16:45 The long time behavior of the fifth-order KdV equations.
(613) **Jun Cao,** University of South Florida, Tampa.

17:30-17:45 .... Break

17:45 Spatially local estimates for semilinear parabolic systems.
(614) **Selwyn Hollis,** Armstrong State College, Savannah.

Problems in Hysteresis (cont.)
14:00–17:30   Room 14
Chaired by: L. Tavernini and A. Visintin

14:00 Numerical methods for ODEs with hysteresis.
(615) **L. Tavernini,** University of Texas at San Antonio, San Antonio.

14:45 PDE's with hysteresis operators.
(616) **A. Visintin,** Universita di Trento, Italy.

15:30-16:00 .... Break

16:00 Dynamics of closed systems with hysteresis.
(617) **A.V. Pokrovskii,** Institute for Information Transmission Problems, Russia.

16:45 Some limit properties for relays.
(618) **T.I. Seidman,** University of Maryland-Baltimore Campus, Baltimore.

Stochastic Systems (cont.)
14:00–17:30   Room 17
Chaired by: N.U. Ahmed

14:00 A stochastic model of an integrable dynamical system.
(619) **Y. Itoh,** Institute of Statistical Mathematics, Japan.

14:45 Nonlinear state estimation from point process observations.
(620) **T.H. Thao,** Universite de Sciences, Algeria.

15:30-16:00 .... Break

16:00 On ergodic theorems for modulated random measures.
(621) **E. Dshalalow,** Florida Institute of Technology, Melbourne.

16:45 Some new results in stochastic reaction diffusion equations.
(622) **M.H. Chang,** University of Alabama, Huntsville.

General (cont.)
14:00–17:30   Room 12
Chaired by: C.T. Fulton

14:00 Oscillation theory for fourth order self-adjoint equations and oscillatory - nonoscillatory classification of singular endpoints.
(623) **Charles T. Fulton*,** Florida Institute of Technology, Melbourne, **Steven Pruess,** Colorado School of Mines, Boulder, and **Limin Wu,** Florida Institute of Technology.

14:45 Some inequalities related to differential equations.
(624) **A. Fink,** Iowa State University, Ames.

15:30-16:00 .... Break

16:00 Classical unified field theory on nonlinear space time.
(625) **A.S. Yu,** Hong Kong Polytech, Hong Kong.

16:45 Linearization of some products of orthogonal polynomials.
(626) **H.M. Srivastava,** University of Victoria, Canada.

Control Systems (cont.)
14:00–16:45   Room B
Chaired by: E. Roxin

14:00 Linearization and approximation of control systems.
(627) **E.O. Roxin,** University of Rhode Island, Kingston.

14:45 Boundary controllability of semilinear differential equations.
(628) **K. Naito,** Senshu University, Japan.

15:30-16:00 .... Break

16:00 The shape design problems for systems with distributive parameters.
(629) **S.P. Ohezin,** Ural State University, Russia.

Bifurcation
14:00-17:30   Room 6
Chaired by: M. Farkas

14:00 Solving nonlinear singular problems and application to bifurcation problems.
(630) **Z.H. Yang,** Shanghai University of Science and Technology, China.

14:45 Bifurcations in a predator-prey model with memory and diffusion.
(631) **M. Farkas,** Budapest University of Technology, Hungary.

15:30-16:00 .... Break

16:00 On the analysis of dynamic bifurcations and stability of solutions.
(632) **K. Huseyin,** University of Waterloo, Canada.

16:45 Nodal structure on global bifurcating solution branches of elliptic systems with symmetry.
(633) **H. Kielhofer**, Institute fur Mathematik, Germany.

Optimization & Optimal Control (cont.)
14:00–19:15   Room 18
Chaired by: S. Aizicovici

14:00 An algorithm for large scale nonlinear optimization problems.
(634) **P.T. Boggs**, Department of Commerce, Gaithersburg.

14:45 Stability of solutions and Lagrange-Newton method for nonlinear optimization and optimal control problems.
(635) **W. Alt**, University of Bayreuth, Germany.

15:30–16:00 ....Break

16:00 Optimal shape design of thin elastic plates and shells with obstacles.
(636) **J. Sokolowski**, Systems Research Institute ofthe Polish Academy, Poland.

16:45 Viscosity solutions of nonlinear equations associated with control problems.
(637) **N. Yamada**, Miyazaki University, Japan.

17:30-17:45 ....Break

17:45 Volterra integral inclusions with applications in optimal control.
(638) **S. Aizicovici**, Ohio University, Athens.

18:30 New approach to the dynamic programming for optimal control problems with state constraints.
(639) **M.M. Khrustalev**, Moscow Aviation Institute, Russia.

Duality and Variational Methods
14:00–17:30   Room C
Chaired by: V.A. Ubhaya

14:00 Duality in approximation.
(640) **V.A. Ubhaya**, North Dakota State University, Fargo.

14:45 Variational methods in nonlinear boundary value problems.
(641) **M. Emmer**, Universita di Roma "La Sapienze", Italy.

15:30–16:00 ....Break

16:00 Variational methods to nonlinear systems and some applications to biomathematics.
(642) **K.N. Murty**, Andhra University, India.

16:45 The minimax principle of mechanics and its applications to optimal control problem for robot manipulators.
(643) **Y.S. Pyatnitskiy**, Institute of Control Sciences, Russia.

Functional Differential Equations
17:40-18:40   Room 1
Chaired by: R. Hering

17:40 On the asymptotic stability of the solutions of functional differential equations with infinite delay.
(644) **G. Makay**, Southern Illinois University, Carbondale.

18:00 Stable periodic solutions in infinite delay systems.
(645) **R. Hering**, University of Missouri, Rolla.

18:20 Uniqueness of slowly oscillating periodic solutions of certain second order delay autonomous differential equation.
(646) **M. Lizana**, Universidad Central de Venezuela, Venezuela.

Math Biology
17:40-19:20   Room 2
Chaired by: L. Fausett

17:40 Global variables and population dynamics: Prey- predator models.
(647) **P. Auger**, University de Bourgogne, France.

18:00 Cellular automata models applied to the study of ventricular tachycardia and fibrillation.
(648) **A. Bardou**, INSERM, France.

18:20 Distabilization of the immune memory attractor by discrete dynamics.
(649) **A. Neumann**, The Weizmann Institute, Israel.

18:40 On Plankton models with delay nutrient recycling.
(650) **S. Ruan**, University of Alberta, Canada.

19:00 A mathematical model of the synchronization of a circadian rhythm in crayfish.
(651) **S. Lopez de Medrano**, Avenida Universidad, Mexico.

Elliptic Partial Differential Equations
17:40-19:20   Room 5
Chaired by: S. Hu

17:40 Quasilinear elliptic systems with singular solutions.
(652) **L. Mou**, University of Southern California, Los Angeles.

18:00 On the Hölder continuous solutions of the Dirichlet problem for degenerate quasi-linear elliptic equations.
(653) **Y. Mizutani**, Nishinippon Institute of Technology, Japan.

18:20 On the existence of radial solutions of a nonlinear elliptic equations on the unit ball.
(654) **Y. Cheng**, University of Uppsala, Sweden.

18:40 On an elliptic system and possibility of non- constant stable solutions.
(655) **S. Jimbo**, Okayama University, Japan.

19:00 Branches of radial solutions for semipositone problems.
(656) **S. Gadam**, University of North Texas, Denton.

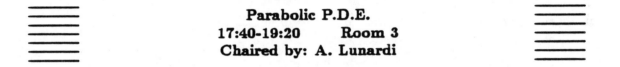

Stability
17:40-19:20   Room 8
Chaired by: S. Köksal

17:40 Lyapunov stability for dynamic systems on time scales.
(657) **B. Kaymakcalan**, Florida Institute of Technology, Melbourne.

18:00 Perturbing Lyapunov functions in large-scale dynamic systems.
(658) **Z. Drici**, Florida Institute of Technology, Melbourne.

18:20 Lipschitz stability of nonlinear matrix differential system.
(659) **S. Köksal**, University of Southwestern Louisiana, Lafayette.

18:40 Practical stability of impulsive control systems.
(660) **F. McRae**, Florida Institute of Technology, Melbourne.

19:00 Monotone iterative technique of impulsive differential systems with variable moments.
(661) **J. Devi**, Florida Institute of Technology, Melbourne.

Parabolic P.D.E.
17:40-19:20   Room 3
Chaired by: A. Lunardi

17:40 Large time behavior of solutions of a singular diffusion equations.
(662) **H. Zhang**, Ball State University, Muncie.

18:00 Existence theory for a strongly degenerate parabolic system.
(663) **X. Xu**, The University of Arkansas, Fayetteville.

18:20 A hierarchy of nonlinear PDE's modeling impurity diffusion in semiconductors.
(664) **W. Richardson**, University of Texas, San Antonio.

18:40 On the existence, stability, and uniqueness of coexistence states for the Lotka-Volterra models with diffusion.
(665) **J. Lopez-Gomez**, Universidad Complutense, Spain.

19:00 Blowing up solutions of semilinear parabolic equations.
(666) **T. Itoh**, Tokai University, Japan.

19:20 Complicated dynamics of scalar reaction diffusion equations with a nonlocal term.
(667) **J. Sefcik**, University of Minnesota, Minneapolis.

ODE (Boundary Value Problems)
17:40-19:20   Room 4
Chaired by: V. Maric

17:40 A boundary value problem with multiple solutions of steady flow in a porous pipe.
(668) **C. Lu**, Southern Illinois University, Edwardsville.

18:00 Periodic boundary value problems for second, third, and higher order ordinary differential equations.
(669) **A. Cabada**, University of Santiago de Compostela, Spain.

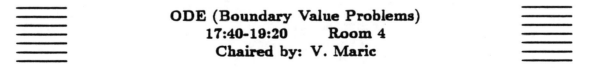

18:20 Existence results for boundary value problems without growth restrictions.
(670) **M. Frigon**, Universita de Montreal, Canada.

18:40 Regularity property of a similarity solution arising in boundary layer theory.
(671) **V. Maric**, University of Novi Sad, Yugoslavia.

19:00 TBA.
(672) **P.S. Kamala**, JPL, Los Angeles.

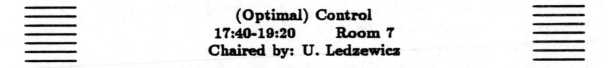

(Optimal) Control
17:40-19:20   Room 7
Chaired by: U. Ledzewicz

17:40 Well-posedness in impulsive control theory.
(673) **F. Rampazzo**, Universita di Padova, Italy.

18:00 On viscosity solutions for nonlinear equations involving nonlocal operators.
(674) **N. Yamada**, Miyazaki University, Japan.

18:20 A new method for global optimal control.
(675) **E. Galperin**, Universite du Quebec a Montreal, Canada.

18:40 Optimality conditions for control of infinite dimensional spaces.
(676) **X. Li** Fudan University, People's Republic of China.

19:00 Bifurcation in optimal control problems.
(677) **Z. Ding**, Nanjing Aeronautical Institute, People's Republic of China.

Variational Methods
17:40-19:00   Room 9
Chaired by: W. Chen

17:40 Distribution of mass principle and its applications.
(678) **W. Chen**, Springfield, Missouri.

18:00 The semiglobal isometric imbedding in $R^2 \to E^3$ with Gaussian curvature changing sign cleanly.
(679) **G. Dong** Zheijiang University, People's Republic of China.

18:20 Limit relative category and critical point theory.
(680) **D. Lupo**, Universita de Trieste, Italy.

18:40 Variational characterization of rotating Euler flows.
(681) **B. Van de Fliert** University of Twente, Netherlands.

Mathematical Physics
17:40-19:00   Room 11
Chaired by: K. Rekab

17:40 A free boundary eigenvalue problem.
(682) **R. Meyer-Spasche**, MPI fur Plasmaphysik, Germany.

18:00 Measure valued solution for non-Newtonian compressible heat conductive monopolar fluid.
(683) **S. Matuso-Necasova**, Czech. Technical University, Czechoslovakia.

18:20 3D solutions of the Peaker and related equations.
(684) **R. Gabdoulline**, Russian Academy of Sciences, Russia.

18:40 Coupling the MHD equations on an interior domain to Maxwell's equations on an exterior domain.
(685) **A. Meir**, Auburn University, Auburn.

Stochastics
17:40-19:00   Room 15
Chaired by: G. Ladde

17:40 Nonlinear stochastic PDE's with monotone nonlinearities.
(686) **F. Flandoli**, Scuola Normale Superiore, Italy.

18:00 Nonlinear filtering algorithm and stochastic dichotomy.
(687) **I. Boguslavsky**, State Research Institute of Aviation Systems, Russia.

18:20 Optimal control of arrival and service rates for two M/M/1 queues in series.
(688) **M. Moustafa**, The American University of Cairo, Egypt.

18:40 On some application of Koenig's theorem and its modification.
(689) **L. Atanassova**, Bulgarian Academy of Sciences, Bulgaria.

Functional Differential Equations
17:40-19:00   Room 1
Chaired by: Q. Huang

17:40 Stability of nonlinear FDE with applications to viscoelasticity of aging bodies.
(690) **A. Drozdov** Hanasi Harishon, Israel.

18:00 Space C^n and permanent coexistence of functional differential equations with infinite delay.
(691) **Q. Huang**, Northeast Normal University, People's Republic of China.

18:20 Approximate solutions of boundary value problems for differential difference equations.
(692) **M. Kurihara**, Yamanashi University, Japan.

18:40 A convexification algorithm for the modeling of nonlinear dynamic processes.
(693) **N. Trinko**, Moscow State University, Russia.

Math Biology
17:40-19:20   Room 2
Chaired by: Y. Gusev

17:40 Mathematical modelling of blood flow through arteries in vibrating environments.
(694) **G. Sharma**, Institute of Basic Science, India.

18:00 Computational analysis of a bursting neuron model.
(695) **R. Bertram**, Florida State University, Tallahassee.

18:20 Effect of stochastic inheritance of cell lifetime on dynamics of cell populations.
(696) **Y. Gusev**, Rutgers University, New Brunswick.

18:40 A cycle of limit cycles in a generalized Gause- type model of two predator feeding on two prey.
(697) **A. Sikder**, Jadavpur University, India.

19:00 Analysis of bilocal immunogenic tumor nonlinear dynamics considering cell migration.
(698) **E. Alekseeva**, RAS Computing Center, Russia.

Elliptic Partial Differential Equations
17:40-19:20   Room 5
Chaired by: H. Gomez

17:40 Decay properties of solutions to semilinear equations.
(699) **A. Rumbos**, Pomana College, Claremont.

18:00 Regularity for solutions of an elliptic equation near nonsmooth interface.
(700) **D. Pahk**, Yonsei University, Korea.

18:20 Estimates of strong solutions to certain quasilinear elliptic problems.
(701) **T. Kuo**, National Hiao Tung University, Taiwan.

18:40 Nonlinear elliptic systems and their applications.
(702) **G. Wen**, Peking University, People's Republic of China.

19:00 On some minimax type values of the functional corresponding to the semilinear elliptic boundary value problems.
(703) **H. Gomez**, Universidad de Los Andes, Colombia.

Stability
17:40-19:00   Room 8
Chaired by: S. Malek

17:40 Sesqui-quasi linearization.
(704) **S. Malek**, Florida Institute of Technology.

18:00 Integral Lipschitz conditions and asymptotic stability.
(705) **T. Wang**, Oakton Community college, Des Plaines.

18:20 On stability analysis of impulsive Lyapunov system.
(706) **K. Murty**, Andhra University, India and **V. Rao**, JNT University College of Engineering, India.

18:40 Roughness of (h,k)-dichotomies.
(707) **M. Pinto** and **R. Naulin***, Universidad de Chile, Chile.

Parabolic PDE
17:40-19:00   Room 12
Chaired by: Y. Chen

17:40 Contact problems on thermo elasticity.
(708) **P. Shi**, Oakland University, Rochester.

18:00 Evolution equations with a free boundary condition.
(709) **Y. Chen**, University of Florida, Gainesville.

18:20 Dynamical behavior of solutions of semilinear heat equation with nonlocal singularity.
(710) **K. Deng**, University of Southwestern Louisiana, Lafayette.

Variational Methods
17:40-19:00   Room 10
Chaired by: S. Terracini

17:40 Periodic solutions to some n-body type problems.
(711) **S. Terracini**, Politecnico di Milano, Italy.

18:00 Multiple solutions and bifurcation for prescribed mean curvature problems.
(712) **C. Chen**, Indiana University, Bloomington.

18:20 Lower semicontinuity and equilibrium points.
(713) **K. Tan** and **X. Yuan**, Dalhousi University, Canada.

18:40 Critical point theory and its applications to nonlinear control theory.
(714) **S. Vakhrameev**, All Union Institute, Russia.

Mathematical Physics
17:40-19:00   Room 13
Chaired by: W. van Horrsen

17:40 Mathematical singularities and superstring dynamics.
(715) **E. Escultura**, University of the Philippines, Philippines.

18:00 Asymptotics for a class of weakly nonlinear wave equations with applications to some problems.
(716) **W. van Horrsen**, University of Delft, Netherlands.

18:20 Wave propogation in a system of couple nonlinear oscillators.
(717) **V. Perez-Munzouri**, Univ. de Santiago de Compostela, Spain.

18:40 Cauchy problem for the Schrodinger equation.
(718) **E. Kaikina**, Moscow State University, Russia.

Stochastics
17:40-18:40   Room 16
Chaired by: M. Sambhandam

17:40 Two parameter stochastic process on nonstandard probability spaces.
(719) **M. Munoz de Ozak**, Universidad Nacional de Colombia, Colombia.

18:00 Weighted inequalities with an arbitrary convex function.
(720) **S. Emara**, The American University of Cairo, Egypt.

18:20 Measure chains.
(721) **S. Hilger**, Institute für Mathematik der, Germany.

Computational Methods
17:40-19:20   Room 18
Chaired by: F. Munger

17:40 Taylor recurrence in analytic ODE's.
(722) **F. Munger**, ACTA Corporation, Cocoa Beach.

18:00 Monte-Carlo simulation in the reaction of $p-p'$- Dinitrodibenzyl electroreduction to $p-p'$-Diaminodibenzyl.
(723) **M. Olea**, University of Clujj-Napoca, Romania.

18:20 Construction of numerical solutoin of permanent waves of two liquids.
(724) **N. Moussa**, The American University of Cairo, Egypt.

18:40 Computing best L^1-simultaneous approximant.
(725) **S. Sahab**, King Abdulaziz University, Saudi Arabia.

19:00 The generalized Newton's method for variational inequalities.
(726) **L.U. Uko**, University of Ibadan, Nigeria.

Mathematical Physics
17:40-19:00   Room 13
Chaired by: J. Porteiro

17:40 Zeeman stability for a class of vecor fields.
(727) **A. Rueda**, Trinyi UT, Hungary.

18:00 An oregonator-based model for the influence of a radial electric field on spiral wave dynamics.
(728) **J. Porteiro***, University of South Florida, and **V. Perez-Villar**, Universidad de Santiago de Compostela, Spain.

18:20 Propogation of two-dimensional bores on the surface of an incompressible fluid.
(729) **S. Rajopadhye**, Pennsylvania State University, University Park.

18:40 The Cauchy problem for the Davey-Stewartson II equation.
(730) **L. Sung**, Clarkson University, Potsdam.

Ordinary Differential Equations
17:40-19:20   Room 1
Chaired by: G. Meisters

17:40 Differential inclusions on graphs.
(731) **D. Bothe**, Universitat Paderborn, Germany.

18:00 Discontinuous approximations to delay differential equations using differential inclusions.
(732) **D. Babai***, Claremont Graduate School, Claremont and **J. Belair**, Universite de Montreal, Canada.

18:20 A bilinear family of eigenvalue problems equivalent to Keller's Jacobian conjecture.
(733) **G. Meisters**, University of Nebraska, Lincoln.

18:40 A shadowing approach to passage through finitely many saddle points.
(734) **C. Ho**, Tunghai University, Taiwan.

19:00 Status of a conjecture on point dissipative nonlinear dynamical systems with conservative terms.
(735) **A. Cover, et al.**, Clemson University, Clemson.

General
17:40-19:20   Room 2
Chaired by: I. Rodrigues

17:40 On rational recursive sequences.
(736) **I. Rodrigues**, The University of Rhode Island, Kingston.

18:00 Periodicity in delay difference systems.
(737) **S. Zhang**, Anhui University, People's Republic of China.

18:20 Smooth approximation of Sobolev function on planar domains.
(738) **A. Stanoyevitch**, University of Hawaii at Manoa, Hawaii.

18:40 TBA.
(739) **S. Wang**, Institute of Systems Science, People's Republic of China.

19:00 On the C^r Morse lemma.
(740) **S. Lopez de Medrano**, Ciudad Universitaria, Mexico.

General
17:40-19:20   Room 9
Chaired by: J. Uvah

17:40 Applications of summability methods.
(741) **Z.U. Ahmad**, Aligarh Muslim University, India.

18:00 Existence and uniqueness results for Volterra integro-differential systems.
(742) **J. Uvah**, University of West Florida, Pensacola.

18:20 Asymptotic equivalence of perturbed linear difference systems.
(743) **R. Medina**, Universidad de Chile, Chile.

18:40 TBA.
(744) **A. Zafer**, Iowa State University, Ames.

19:00 TBA
(745) **H.K. Pathak**, Kalyan Mahavidyalaya, India.

Fixed Points
17:40-19:00   Room 15
Chaired by: D. Violette

17:40 Fixed point principles for cones of Banach space for multivalued maps differentiable at the origin and the infinity.
(746) **D. Violette**, Universite de Moncton, Canada.

18:00 The random product of two nonexpansive mappings in spaces with opial property.
(747) **T. Kuczumorov**,

18:20 A new Z_p index theory via Z_p Borsuk-Ulam theorem.
(748) **Z.Q. Wang**, Utah State University, Logan.

18:40 Existence and uniqueness theorems of coupled fixed points and applications.
(749) **K. Lan**, University of Puget Sound, Tacoma.

Nonlinear Operators
17:40-19:20   Room 16
Chaired by: K. Tan

17:40 Weighted Sobelev spaces and Nemitsky operators.
(750) **S. Leonardi**, University of Catania, Italy.

18:00 A nonlinear ergodic theorem for almost orbits of nonlinear contraction of semigroups in Banach spaces.
(751) **K. Tan**, Dalhousie University, Canada.

18:20 TBA.
(752) **G. Bognar**, Miskolc University, Hungary.

18:40 Nonlinear Fredholm mappings and bifurcations in the Pleateau problem.
(753) **A. Borisovich,** Voronez State University, Russia.

19:00 Nonlinear operators of local type with applications to stochastic analysis.
(754) **A. Ponosov,** Ruhr-Universitat Bochum, Germany.

Stability
17:40-18:40   Room 8
Chaired by: R.I. Kozlov

17:40 Differential inequality for comparison method by vector functions of Lyapunov-Razumiohin-Lakshmikantham type.
(755) **R.I. Kozlov,** Irkutsk Computing Center, Russia.

18:00 Comparison approach for stability analysis of functional differential equations with using critical comparison system.
(756) **N.I. Matrosova,** Irkutsk Computing Center, Russia.

18:20 Lyapunov-Lagrange method for optimal control problems of partially observable dynamical systems.
(757) **S.V. Savastuk,** Moscow Branch IPT, Russia.

Elliptic Partial Differential Equations
17:40-19:20   Room 17
Chaired by: J. Gamez

17:40 Barrier method for even order elliptic equations.
(758) **Y. Furusho,** Saga University, Japan.

18:00 Existence and uniqueness of positive solutions of the nonlinear singular boundary value problems.
(759) **G. Hernandez,** University of Connecticut, Storrs.

18:20 On the Dirichlet problems.
(760) **H. Wang,** National Tsing Hua University, Taiwan.

18:40 Some remarks about the existence of positive solutions for elliptic systems.
(761) **J. Gamez,** University of Granada, Spain.

19:00 Upper and lowe solutions of nonlinear elliptic and parabolic problems.
(762) **K. Singh,** Institute of Informatics, Hungary.

Parabolic PDE
17:40-18:40   Room 12
Chaired by: D. Jackson

17:40 An existence and uniqueness theorem for solutions of nonlocal parabolic partial differential equations.
(763) **D. Jackson,** Florida Institute of Technology, Melbourne.

18:00 Theorem about a weak impulsive nonlinear parabolic differential inequality together with weak impulsive nonlocal nonlinear inequalities.
(764) **L. Byszewski,** Florida Institute of Technology, Melbourne.

18:20 Stefan problems in several space variables with dynamic boundary conditions.
(765) **T. Aiki**, Nagasaki Institute of Applied Science, Japan.

Engineering Applications
17:40-19:20   Room 10
Chaired by: N. Tepedelenlioglu

17:40 Subharmonic hysteresis in nonlinear optical systems.
(766) **I. Schwartz**, Naval Research Laboratory, Washington.

18:00 Tracking unstable periodic orbits in experiments: A new continuation method.
(767) **I. Triandaf**, U.S. Naval Research Laboratory, Washington.

18:20 Nonlinear vibration analysis of a skew panel under elevated temperature.
(768) **P. Biswas**, P: D: Women's College, India.

18:40 Nonlinear analysis of irregular shaped plates vibrating at large amplitude.
(769) **M. Banerjee**, A.C. College, India.

19:00 Stochastic stability and bifurcation analysis for gated radar range trackers.
(770) **R. Gover**, Tactical Electronic Warfare Div., Washington.

Mathematical Physics
17:40-19:00   Room 13
Chaired by: X. Liu

17:40 Products of distributions in mathematical physics.
(771) **A. Palanques-Mestre**, University of Barcelona, Spain.

18:00 Overstable convection in rotating layer.
(772) **A. Shayganmanesh**, Iran University of Science and Technology, Iran.

18:20 Asymptotic behavior for large time of solutions to the Korteweg-DeVries equation with weak dissipation.
(773) **P. Naumkin**, Moscow State University, Russia.

18:40 Nonlinear aspects in analysis and computation for semiconductor devices.
(774) **F. Alabau**, Universite Bordeaux I, France.

General
17:40-18:20   Room 2
Chaired by: A. Ize

17:40 Double ended queue via diffusion approximation.
(775) **M. Jain**, Institute of Basic Science, India.

18:00 Linear asymptotically autonomous neutral functional differential equations with multiple eigenvalues.
(776) **A. Ize**, Univ. de Sao Paulo, Brazil.

18:20 Approximation methods for eigenvalue problems of second kind Fredholm integral equation.
(777) **E. Lin**, The University of Toledo, Toledo.

ODE
17:40-19:00   Room 1
Chaired by: H. Onose

17:40 The measure centre, the minimal centre, and the weakly almost periodic point.
(778) **Z. Zhou**, Zhongshang University, People's Republic of China.

18:00 On nonlinear boundary value problems for multi-valued differential equations with interface conditions in Banach spaces.
(779) **S. Mazen**, College Misericordia, Dallas.

18:20 Periodic solutions of second order impulsive integro-differential system.
(780) **E. Liz**, Universidad de Vigo, Spain.

18:40 Oscillation of nonlinear first order differential equation and its applications.
(781) **H. Onose**, Ibaraki University, Japan.

General
17:40-19:20   Room 9
Chaired by: P.L. Felmer

17:40 Subharmonics near an equilibrium for some second order Hamiltonian systems.
(782) **P.L. Felmer**, Universidad de Chile, Chile.

18:00 On the inversion of functions.
(783) **G. Zampieri**, Universita di Padova, Italy.

18:20 Calculation of unsteady turbulent flows over oscillating flap.
(784) **S.W. Kim*, T.J. Benson, D.J. McKenzie, and F.R. Payne**, NASA, Ames.

18:40 Biochemical threshold-logic device capable of storing short memory: Application to neural network study and practical implementation of device.
(785) **M. Okamoto*, Y. Maki, and T. Sekiguchi**, Kyushu Institute of Technology, Japan.

19:00 Interfacial wave theory of dendritic crystal growth and its comparison with experiments.
(786) **J.J. Xu**, McGill University, Canada.

List of Speakers

Numbers following the names indicate the speakers' positions on the program

Abed, E.H 477
Acker, A. 145
Adomaitis, R. 478
Adomian, G 372, 453
Agarwal, R.P 52
Agur, Z. 391
Ahlebrandt, C. 53
Ahmad, I.A. 449, 609
Ahmad, S. 234
Ahmad, Z.U. 741
Ahmed, N.U. 549
Ahn, H. 94
Aiki, T. 181, 765
Aizicovici, S. 638
Alabau, F. 774
Albeverio, S. 306
Alekseeva, E. 698
Allen, L.S. 150
Alt, W. 635
Altman, W. 399
Amann, H. 303
An der Heiden, U. 540
Anderson, J.R. 182
Andersson, S.I. 494
Ang, D.D. 77
Anger, G. 359
Antman, S. 288
Antoniou, I. 20
Appell, J. 165
Astumian, R. Dean 277
Atanassova, L. 689
Aubin, J.P. 6
Auger, P. 316, 647
Aulbach, B. 54
Avrin, J.D. 237
Azbelev, N.V. 107
Babai, D. 732
Badiale, M. 160
Baggerly, K. 384
Bajzer, Z. 493
Bajic, V.B. 474
Balis, U.J. 65
Ballion, J.B 46
Banarjee, M.M 769
Banks, H.T 153
Bardou, A. 648
Bartsch, T. 45, 387
Battelli, F. 454
Bebernes, J. 238
Becker, R.I. 476
Bednarczuk, E. 420

Belair, J. 541, 732
Benilan, Ph. 442
Bensoussan, A. 12
Berezansky, Yu. M. 133
Bernadou, M. 396
Bernfeld, S. 464
Bertram, R. 695
Bielewicz, E. 397
Binding P. 560
Bini, D. 426
Bishop, A. 256
Biswas, P. 768
Bloom, F. 338
Boggs, P.T. 634
Bognar, G. 752
Boguslavsky, I. 687
Bohm, M. 74
Bohme, R. 469
Bona, J. 188
Borisovich, A.Yu. 753
Borisovich, Y.G 262
Borwein, J.M. 125
Bothe, D. 731
Brauer, F. 379
Bressan, A. 500
Brewer, D. 335
Brezis, H. 31
Brokate, M. 535
Brock, W. 32
Browder, F. 29, 463
Bruck, R.E. 47
Burns, S.A. 571
Burton, T.A 114
Busenberg, S.N. 283
Bushell, P.J. 41
Byszewski, L. 764
Cabada, A. 669
Calvert, B.D. 528
Campbell, S.L. 450
Cantrell, S. 92
Cannon, J.R. 264
Cao, J. 613
Carpenter, G. 588
Carroll, R.W. 375
Carl, S. 102
Cascante, M. 572
Castillo-Chavez, C. 382
Cellina, A. 503
Chan, C.Y. 57
Chandna, O.P. 187
Chang K.C. 583

Chang M.H. 622
Chapman, S.J. 326
Charalambous, C. 575
Chatelin, F. 353
Chen, Y. 709
Chen, W. 678
Chen, C. 712
Cheng, S.S. 55
Cheng, Y. 654
Chernousko, F.L. 19
Chipot, M. 301
Chiu, C. 392
Chhabra, A. 337
Choudhury, S.R. 185
Chow, P.L. 550
Chua, Leou 1, 109
Chukwu, E. 60
Clement, P. 435
Cobelli, C. 517
Colonius, F. 61
Corduneanu, C. 296, 465
Corless, M. 519
Costa, D. 566
Coti Zelati, V. 269
Coughran, Jr., W.M. 253
Cover, A. 735
Cronin-Scanlon, J. 17, 82
Crowe, K. 151
Damlamian, A. 443
Dancer, E.N. 302
Debussche, A. 210
DeClaris N. 585
Demetrios, L. 64
Demongeot, J. 63
Deng, B. 455
Deng, K. 710
Desch, W. 434
Dibos, F. 243
Ding, T. 320
Ding, Z. 677
Dolezal, J. 344
Dong, G. 679
Dontchev, A.L. 126
Dorodnitsyn, V.A. 106
Dorofeuk, A.A. 368
Drabek, P. 71
Drakhlin, M. 418
Drici, Z. 658
Drozdov, A. 690
Dshalalow, E. 621
Du, Q. 323